LITTLE DOG LOST

K. Suzanne Moorhouse

Illustrated by Chet Jezierski

Honey's Story is a work of fiction. The characters and situations in this story are imaginary. No resemblance is intended between these characters and any real persons, either living or dead.

First published 1997 by
The Book Guild Ltd.
25 High Street,
Lewes, Sussex

Second Printing 2002

0-9521109-1-1

Set in Times

Typesetting by Raven Typesetters, Chester

Printed in Great Britain by
Bookcraft (Bath) Ltd. Avon

CONTENTS

LITTLE DOG LOST

LITTLE DOG LOST

INTRODUCTION

I had a Bearded Collie called Rory as a child and with my family, tried to find another one to replace him when he died of old age – sadly with no luck.

On leaving school, I decided I would like to go into horses in some way. My mother was not so keen on the idea and suggested what about dogs instead? I thought this a good idea so, deciding that Poodles were very nice little dogs, I went down to a kennels in London for 12 months' training to learn all the ropes such as trimming, breeding and showing. Whilst I was in training, I bought my first two Poodles, one of which was a show dog. It naturally followed then to buy the Dog Annuals (magazines that come out each year-end full of advertisements for everything in the dog world from dogs to leads and collars, with everything in between).

There, in the first annual I bought, was a picture of a kennel maid holding about six Bearded Collies. I immediately wrote to the breeder of the Beardies and asked if I could buy a puppy and was delighted to receive the reply that as soon as a bitch puppy was available I could have her.

After seven, of what seemed to a very impatient person exceptionally long, months, a letter arrived from Mrs Willison, the breeder and owner of the Bothkennar Beardies, telling me my puppy had been born.

Mrs Willison had spent many years reviving the breed from virtual extinction and was considered the best authority on Beardies. She wrote asking me if I could collect my puppy at seven weeks old, instead of eight weeks (the time she usually let puppies leave for their new homes), as she had a holiday booked.

I was delighted. I would have collected my new puppy at five weeks old if it had been possible, but had expected to wait for the full eight weeks, so one week early was a real bonus.

When you breed dogs, and get yourself established as a breeder, you can apply to the Kennel Club for your own kennel name. It's fairly complicated and can be a costly procedure. At the time I acquired Barberry, a kennel name could be used as either a prefix or affix (i.e. either before the name you choose for registering your puppy, or after it). Mrs Willison's was Bothkennar, mine is Willowmead. The Kennel Club changed the system some years later and the breeder, that is the person who owns the bitch at the time the litter is born, can now only use their name as a prefix whereas if you buy a puppy in, it is only possible to put your name at the end of the puppy's name. When I bought Barberry of Bothkennar I promptly placed my prefix in front so consequently her registered name was Willowmead Barberry of Bothkennar, much too much of a mouthful for a call name at home. I usually prefer to call my dogs by their registered name and as Barberry was an easy name to say and, most important of all, suited her really well, Barberry she became.

The aim of all dedicated breeders is to produce a dog that is as near as possible to the breed standard, which is a description of that particular dog – as near, that is, as is humanly possible to get, or as near perfect as nature will allow.

Breeding livestock can be a fascinating hobby as the

4

perfect dog has never been born. You will always be endeavouring to achieve it: looking at dogs, studying pedigrees, working out what you hope will produce the ultimate dog of your chosen breed.

I collected Barberry from Mrs Willison. She was all I could wish for and I made her into my first champion. So, I started breeding Beardies as well as my Poodles which I was well-established in by now.

Years slowly passed and 1971 dawned bright and clear. By this time, I was on my fifth generation of Beardies, all direct descendants of the original Barberry. I had bought in a bitch called Broadholme Cindy Sue, to which I added 'of Willowmead' as usual to her registered name to establish in her pedigree that I owned her for future generations. Cindy Sue was a daughter of my own dog Ruairidh of Willowmead and a Bothkennar bitch called Bobby's Girl. Cindy Sue also reminded me very much of her famous forebear and, as I thought Cindy Sue was a name more suited to a Poodle, decided I would call my new puppy Barberry. She really lived up to her name and was very much like the first Barberry in disposition and habits so it proved a happy choice. I also made her into a champion too.

WILLOWMEAD SUPER HONEY

Honey was a golden-brown Bearded Collie of exceptional qualities. Even her arrival into this world was different. She was born nine days early. The usual time a bitch is in whelp is nine weeks or approximately sixty-three days. It is not unusual for her to whelp anything from five days early to five days over but nine days is very early indeed and can easily result in the death of all the puppies. Barberry, Honey's mother, had already had one litter which produced some very nice puppies. I had mated her, for her second litter, to a champion dog called Wishanger Cairnbhan, famous for his lovely temperament and super dark-brown coat. Barberry was a slate-grey and I hoped to get both brown and slate-grey puppies from the expected litter.

As it was some time before Barberry was due to whelp, I had gone down to a dog show in London which involved getting up at around three in the morning and driving the 130 miles, getting home about eight-thirty or so at night. My brother Michael had travelled with me. When we arrived home, my mother, who was looking after the dogs left at home, told me Barberry had been very restless all day but had eaten all her dinner. As a bitch usually goes off her food immediately prior to whelping, I was not unduly concerned but said I would get the whelping box into the kitchen. I always whelp my bitches in the kitchen, it's warm there and the kettle is handy for the inevitable cups of tea if you have to wait for hours should things go slowly. So, I duly brought in the big box and filled it with newspapers — useful as you can change them as necessary and the bitches love to chew and scratch them up to small pieces to make their nests. Barberry, who knew exactly what the box was for, hopped in and settled down to get what I hoped would be a good night's rest.

I also went to bed, very tired after a long and busy day at the show, and immediately fell into a deep sleep. At about six o'clock next morning I woke up, well refreshed, and heard a noise like the brakes of a lorry going round the very bad bend on the nearest road to our house. The noise made me suddenly think of Barberry. Was it a lorry or my dog? I popped my dressing-gown on and trotted downstairs. There was Barberry sitting in her box having, as it turned out, puppy number seven. I very rapidly went to help her and she soon had the other two, making a litter of nine: six boys and three girls. All three girls were brown as were three of the boys too, with three slate-grey boys. The puppies were very tiny and obviously very premature. Their noses and paws were very pink and quite bald whereas full-term puppies are fully covered with hair at birth and a normal colour too.

As soon as it was a reasonable time of morning, I called the vet to come and check Barberry over to make sure everything was all right and that we had no retained afterbirth or even puppies. When the vet came out, I told him the puppies were actually nine days early. He told me we would be very lucky if any of them lived as they were too early. That did not cheer me up at all but he did not count on what a splendid mother Barberry was. She reared seven of her puppies. The smallest of the bitches got an infection through her cord, so we lost her, as we did a small dog

7

which Barberry was determined should not live as she overlaid him. We found him several times underneath her and fished him out and revived him but she was very determined and in the end squashed him flat. I always feel mothers know best and if they overlay a puppy it could be something we cannot see, some internal problem perhaps. So consequently we ended up with seven beautiful puppies.

As soon as I had sorted out what was what, after changing the box and making Barberry comfortable, I picked Honey out as the one I wanted to keep. I already had my puppy's name planned. I had bred her grandmother and called her Willowmead My Honey. My Honey managed to win her championship with ease. This puppy was to be called Willowmead Super Honey and would, I hoped as I looked at the sleek chestnut-brown baby feeding contentedly, become a champion the same as both her father and mother and her famous grandmother, Champion My Honey.

The babies grew apace and it soon transpired that Honey was going to be a puppy with a difference. She was developing very high intelligence even in a breed of great intelligence. Beardies are dogs that have worked sheep and cattle for centuries and have been renowned for their cleverness in all manner of droving as well as all normal work with their shepherd masters.

The other puppies of the litter left for their new homes and Honey joined the other big dogs as a household pet. Honey soon found there were mice living in the banks of the moat that surrounded our house and would spend ages stalking them. She caught her first mouse when she was just five months old. Barberry had always been a great rabbiter and I thought her daughter was showing good signs of following in Mother's footsteps. Barberry also had a good game of going into the bales of straw, under the

Dutch barn in the stockyard just outside our garden, and chasing out the chicken that was trying to lay her eggs in peace there. You would hear an indignant squawk and out of her nest in the straw would shoot a chicken, wings flapping, and into the nest would disappear half a Beardie, tail wagging furiously only to reappear with her mouth full of hens' eggs. Honey soon learnt that fresh eggs tasted delicious and would happily join her mother on the stockyard raids. A taste that was to stand her in good stead later on in her life.

Other eggs Honey developed a taste for were moorhens' eggs. The moat surrounding the garden ran into a small pool and although the moat would dry up in summer, the pool never did. In springtime there was usually plenty of water in the moat and Honey, who was born in November, had the time of her life round the moat. When she was very small, she was fascinated by the water flowing slowly along and quite early on in her short life she fell into it but was not to be deterred. The very next day she visited the moat again. She cautiously crept down the sloping side, sniffing, her small back feet tensed and ready to leap backwards should the water be too much of a terror after the shock of the previous day. This time however, she did not fall in. Needless to say, she soon found the water was great fun and would often have wet paws when she turned up at the house later on.

Several moorhens had built their nests at the edge of the pool and Honey, who had already learnt the smell and super taste of eggs, sniffed them out. Tiptoeing carefully, as the pool had much deeper water than the moat, she reached the nest and polished off the eggs. It didn't matter that the moorhen was squawking; the chickens did that too and still returned to lay another egg. The moorhens decided enough was enough and built the next nest right in the middle of the pool, well out of a naughty puppy's reach.

Honey had another little trick which she performed each morning. Whenever she came back from her walk with the older Beardies, over the fields and woods surrounding the farm, she would dash into the kitchen where there were about four dog beds in convenient corners all complete with a nice cosy blanket. Honey would trot from bed to bed, collect all the blankets, plonk them all together in one bed and, with the last one hanging from her mouth, climb on top of the pile and sit there smiling as if to say: 'Am I not a clever dog? This is the best bed ever.' You just could not be cross with her as she looked so funny sitting there all pleased with herself.

Honey's early promise of super conformation was developing beautifully. Her movement was a joy to watch. Everyone loved her. She was such a happy puppy and her life was one round of fun. She played hide-and-seek in the spinney and in the cypress trees round the lawn. She dug a little hole under one tree where branches came down to the ground. There she collected all her toys and precious bits which comprised odd balls, sundry old bones and a few rattly tins. She would fetch them out, toss them into the air then race around with them in her mouth until she was tired, but she always put them back into their little hole when she had finished with them.

You can start showing a puppy at six months in England and so Honey was trained to show, which she picked up exceptionally quickly. The show-training involves training the puppy to walk on a loose lead in either the left or right hand but mainly left, to walk in either a circle or straight lines in the shape of a triangle, to remain balanced turning sharp corners, never to pull in any direction and to stand quite still for the judge to handle her all over to check her conformation and lastly, to stand, sometimes for several minutes whilst the judge would look at the whole class prior to making his final decision. Honey took far less time to pick up all her show procedure than the usual puppies I had trained and I was very pleased with her. She also thoroughly enjoyed the training. I then entered her for her first few shows. She was to attend a couple of open shows, before she made her championship show debut, just to see how she would do. Open shows usually have 1,500 to 2,000 dogs whereas the Championship Shows can have up to 15,000 to 18,000 dogs and can be over several days.

Honey and I went off to her first show. She behaved beautifully and won second in her class. A couple of weeks later, we went to her second show. This time she won first and still not seven months old. This was going to be my star, I was sure.

We lived at the time, in a village some 20 miles from a range of hills called the Malverns: a large area rising up to over 1,000 feet – all National Trust land. There are several small towns built around the hills, the largest being called Great Malvern, with West Malvern, as its name would suggest, on the west side of the hills. Malvern Link is on the road towards Worcester, the nearest big town. My dentist was at Malvern Link. I was in the habit of going each week to take the dogs for walks over the hills and, whenever I went to the dentist, would always take the dogs over the hills afterwards. I lived at home with my mother and two brothers. My grandmother of 89 was also staying with us as she had been for several years. Honey was just coming up to seven and a half months old at the time and my mother had a dental appointment so as usual, I took her to the dentist, dropped her off and, with Grandmother in the car, said I would collect my mother in half an hour, after taking the dogs for a quick walk over the hills.

It was a beautiful day in early June. I drove up to the usual carpark called the Clock Tower Carpark because of the huge clock tower at one end of the carpark. I had

Honey, Greta — a ten-month-old Beardie who was also brown but now turning pale, (almost all Beardies change colour, going lighter up to twelve months old then steadily going darker till three years or so when they have their final adult coat, either slate or brown or any of the many colours in between), Juno, who had a litter of five-week-old puppies; Barberry; and two Poodles with me so we had quite a car-full.

I let all the dogs out in the carpark, leaving the car in the shade of some lovely big trees with my grandmother sitting contentedly with all the doors open and walked straight up North Hill on the usual route that I took the dogs. The path starts wide going steadily up in slow curves round the base of the hill. About ten minutes up the wide path a small track goes directly up the hillside. That is the way I always took the dogs to rejoin the wider path much higher up.

We very rarely saw anyone on these walks, most people stayed on the bottom path or went to the main hill of the range called the Beacon where there was a snack-bar at the very topmost point. We had gone round to the far side of North Hill overlooking the western side, rather than the east side where I had left the car and Grandmother. I decided I must go back after a short walk as my mother would soon be out from her appointment at the dentist's so turned round and, calling all the dogs, started to return to the car. The northern part of the Malverns has large valleys and you follow the path in long sweeps from one valley, round the ridge to the next valley. We had just gone round the ridge into a large valley, walking along the path with high bracken on the hill slopes on either side of the path.

I noticed an elderly man walking towards me; he carried a walking-stick in his hand and strode out at a good pace. I called all the dogs back towards me but Beardies are very friendly dogs and some of them went towards him, tails wagging, to say Hello. Obviously, the fellow did not like dogs and ignored them. I dropped off the path, as it was very narrow at that point, to go past him calling the dogs to me as I went. He walked on along the path waving his stick towards any of the dogs near to him. Once past I thought I had better check I had all the dogs with me so I counted them. All present except one – Honey. She had been behind me as I dropped off the path but now was nowhere to be seen. I immediately called her. She was always a most obedient puppy coming the minute she was called. The man was still striding away along the path. Then I saw a small frightened face peep round the ridge, see the man who had nearly reached her and, further on, see me well behind the fellow who waved the stick at her in a most alarming way. She fled in the opposite direction, disappearing from sight. I started to run towards her calling, 'Honey! Honey!'

Very soon I reached the ridge and saw before me a large valley, absolutely empty. No man. No Honey. Simply nothing. I ran right round the valley, round the next ridge, looking up the hill and down the hill for any sign of either the man or my poor frightened puppy. There was simply nothing. I carried on, thinking *she must stop soon*. I went up the hill, down the hill and round the hill for the next hour searching, calling, looking. but my beautiful puppy had vanished into thin air.

I was beginning to get desperate by now. My grandmother was still in the car and must be worrying as to where I had gone to and Juno needed to go to her puppies. We had been away far too long and goodness knows what my mother would be thinking. I had promised to collect her in half an hour, not well over an hour. I would have to go back down the hill and sort things out.

So once again, calling all the dogs, I rushed down the hill to find my grandmother a bit worried but still quite content in the car. I told her I had lost Honey but that we had better go and find my mother before anything else could be done. I drove back down to Malvern Link to find my mother furiously walking up and down the road outside the dentist. She was very cross indeed but when I said I had lost Honey she realised how upset I was and soon calmed down. We drove back up to the Clock Tower Carpark. I said I would have one last look to see if Honey had reappeared in the area where I had lost her. I left the other dogs in the car with my mother and grandmother and I rushed up the hills calling all the way. Still no sign whatsoever of Honey, so sadly I retraced my steps because I had to get Juno back to her puppies.

We all drove home in a very depressed state. When we arrived, I took Juno straight to her puppies and then fed the other dogs. My mother cooked dinner and my brothers, Michael and John, both came home from work and were told the bad news. Both boys said that as soon as we had finished dinner they would go back with me and see if we could find Honey. With three of us looking we could cover more ground. Maybe she had got over her bad fright and regained her usual happy disposition. I was worried that she might just run and run for miles. She had gone towards the west and, in a somewhat fevered imagination, I saw her going on forever right on into Wales, eventually reaching the sea, maybe even swimming out towards Ireland.

Notwithstanding all these foolish thoughts, my brothers and I drove back the 20 miles to Malvern and, for the third time that day, I climbed the steep slope of North Hill and called and called my naughty puppy's name in the vain hope she might come trotting along the path, her face one big smile, or maybe somewhat shamefaced, knowing she had been naughty to run off and cause so much worry. But, although we combed the hills from one end of the range to the other, from top to bottom and every nook and cranny in

15

between, looking, walking and calling until nearly midnight, not even the smallest sign of hide or hair did we see of a small brown Bearded Collie puppy called Honey. At midnight we had to give up the fruitless search and return home, all very tired and, speaking for myself, extremely depressed and worried. Sheep belonging to local farmers graze on the Malvern Hills. I was very concerned that, if Honey was still on the hills or in the near area, she would be seen by some farmer and shot to prevent her from sheep-worrying. I had often read of dogs being shot in the area and I dreaded such a fate befalling my puppy.

REWARD!

The Malverns are a range of hills about 4½ miles long. They rise steeply out of the flat vale of Evesham to the east but to the west the view is over rolling hills stretching out towards the mountains of Wales. At the north end is the Clock Tower Carpark from which the path goes up North Hill to the next hill in the range called the Beacon, which is the highest hill. It slowly goes down to smaller hills with the last one being called British Camp, an ancient burial ground. The main town is Great Malvern which nestles under the Beacon with Malvern Link on the main approach road from Worcester and West Malvern being a straggle of houses and schools with just the odd shop or two going along the western slopes of the hills.

The hills are cared for by the Malvern Hills Conservators. Paths are kept built up whilst bracken and gorse is cut back to save them from growing rampant.

The Beacon boasts a snack-bar on its topmost peak which is very popular with the many people who walk the hills daily. There is also a slightly larger tearoom much lower down on a path directly out of Great Malvern town, with a short and not too steep walk up the hills, called Saint Anne's Well which has, as its name suggests, a spring and well of beautiful clear drinking-water. The local farmers have ancient grazing rights for their sheep on

17

the hills which helps keep the grass short and you can never walk over the hills without seeing sheep in some place or other. There is also an old quarry, worked out long ago, with barbed wire to make sure nobody goes over the very long drop which is on the Clock Tower side of North Hill.

During the night, whilst I could not sleep for worrying about what my poor puppy was doing, I worked out a plan of campaign for the next day. The first port of call would have to be the local police station to see if, by any lucky chance, she had been caught by someone and handed in. The second call must be to all the farmers in the district. June is the time when there are a lot of lambs around and farmers can be inclined to shoot dogs that are obviously alone and wandering amongst their sheep. I did not think there was the least chance Honey would chase sheep with the intent to kill or even harm them, but some farmers don't stop to ask questions. Therefore, farmers had to be contacted and quickly.

I thought, with a bit of annoyance, that Beardies were still a very rare breed of dog. It would be no use telling people that I had lost a Bearded Collie. All but the exception would not have the slightest idea of what a Beardie looked like. I thought it might be helpful to go round the shops and post offices in the more outlying villages and put a small advertisement in the windows with either a sketch or a photo of a Beardie. The local vet would also be a good place. All vets have a notice-board in the waiting-room and the people visiting a vet would definitely be animal-minded and, hopefully, keep an eye open for her. Thinking about the vets reminded me of the local ring-craft club in Malvern. I would find out where they were and ask them to keep an eye open too. They would be mainly breeders who would be most sensible in trying to catch her if they did see her. The last thing I thought of were the local papers. They would get to the greatest amount of people. I would also try television. I had once sold a puppy to a Mr Lenton and he had lost his dog. Mr Lenton had worked for a television company so had managed to have it put out on the local programme which had very rapidly resulted in the dog being found and recaptured only ten days after he had disappeared. Surely I would get Honey back equally quickly. At this stage, I could not think of anything else I could do so I finally fell asleep.

The next morning was bright and clear. At least Honey had not had bad weather for her first night out. As soon as I had fed and exercised all my other dogs and attended to the puppies, I left home for the Malverns on the first of many journeys. I decided to clock the mileage on the car, something I had never bothered to do before. It was exactly 20 miles there, so a 40-mile round trip. As soon as I arrived in Malvern I went straight to the police station and asked if, by any chance, they had had a pale-brown fluffy dog handed in, hoping against hope that my quest might end before it had begun.

No came back the answer to dash the slight hope before it could really take root. So, instead, I gave all the details. Seven and a half months old, a long-coated pale-brown bitch of a very rare breed. Was she valuable? Yes, a very valuable show dog who had already won first prize at shows. How valuable? To which I said the first thing that came into my mind, between £500 and £1,000 which in 1971 was a very high price indeed. The attitude of the police changed at once from one of boredom at just another lost dog, which must have been a daily occurrence in a beauty spot where hundreds of people visit at weekends and holidays. As I still thought Honey might have gone miles in her dash of fear, I suddenly wondered if it would be the normal thing for police stations to contact each other or not. I decided I had better ask and find out exactly what the procedure was.

'No,' said the constable. 'If a dog was handed in to the Malvern station, only the Malvern station would know about it.'

I was dismayed. Honey could be handed in anywhere, would serve her mandatory seven days then be either re-homed if she was lucky or, if not, be put down. I asked if it would be possible to find out if she was at any other station without going to every one. Luckily the constable, told me that, because she was a very valuable show dog, he would telex all the stations in the area with her details and have the news sent directly to the Malvern station if she should be caught. He took my name and address and promised to phone me at once if or when he had any more news.

So my first task was accomplished, in one way very satisfactorily — the next best thing to finding Honey, at least. I then started on the second of my tasks, the local farmers. I decided that, as she had disappeared on the west side that would be the side I would start on. I drove till I saw the first farmhouse, parked in front of the house, knocked at the door and met the farmer's wife. I duly explained about losing Honey, gave her a brief descrip-tion, showed her a photo and begged her to ask her hus-band not to shoot Honey as I was sure she would not harm any sheep. The lady was most sympathetic and, after writ-ing my telephone number down, promised she would keep a good eye open for Honey, tell her husband all about her and one of them would definitely ring me at once if they had any news at all. I felt very cheered by my kind recep-tion and went on my way somewhat more hopeful. Surely someone would see her soon. I travelled on to every farm I could find, telling the same story at every door and unfailingly having a kind and helpful reception.

At every small shop and post office, I stopped and called

in with my story and put small advertisements in their windows, offering a reward for information leading to Honey's recapture and return home. Everybody was so kind I really began to feel I must find her soon. I ended up back in Great Malvern after doing a round trip of the whole range of hills. I had purchased a bar of chocolate from one of the shops for lunch and noticed that, by now, it was around two-thirty. The vet would probably be holding his afternoon surgery so I might catch him before he left for his last calls. I asked at a shop where the local vet's house was. Luckily I was quite near so rapidly drove there. I saw the receptionist and once again told my tale. She was very sorry to hear about poor Honey's plight and said she was only too happy to put up my little notice and sketch – I had by now run out of photographs. Just as she was doing so, the vet came out of his surgery, his last client having left, so once again I told my tale. Oh dear! he was not terribly encouraging. How old did I say? Only seven months! He would give her a week to live if nobody picked her up; she was too much of a baby to survive for long on her own. I left there with my heart in my boots, after feeling there was a good chance that I should soon have Honey back. It was terrible news to be told that she could not survive for more than a week. I decided I would go straight back up to the hills and have another look for her.

I drove back round to North Hill. I parked in the Clock Tower Carpark thinking, you never know, maybe she will see the car and I will find her waiting by it when I get back, ready to jump in and go home. Again, I climbed the path and called and called. I walked over the increasingly familiar ground, peering into every nook and crevice in case Honey should be hiding there. I noticed a dead sheep lying in the bracken about 6 feet down from the path. I immediately thought, help! I hope that's not Honey's

21

work, but on looking more carefully could see it had obviously been dead for several days so definitely could not be anything to do with Honey, thank goodness. Needless to say, there was absolutely no sign of any honey-coloured Beardie anywhere to be seen.

I dared not stay up on the hills for too long as I had to get to the local newspapers to put my advertisements in for them to come out as soon as possible. Most papers were weekend ones, except the *Evening News* which was a daily one. I retraced my steps down the hill to the car and drove, somewhat despondently, back into Worcester to the newspaper offices. I placed advertisements offering the usual reward in all those covering the Malvern and Worcester area. *The Berrows*, which was a weekly paper, was very interested and decided to run an article on it. Perhaps there wasn't much news that week but a good dog story was always well-covered in those days, especially in a farming area. I begged them to put a photograph in, as I mentioned that no one would know what a Beardie would look like, but it seemed there wasn't room for that, or perhaps the story was not quite newsworthy enough for a photo. I was delighted to have an article though, that would be seen by all that read the newspaper, whereas an advertisement would only be read by people looking at that part of the paper.

By this time, it was getting on for six o'clock and I really had to go home to attend to all my other dogs. I simply could not leave my poor mother to do everything.

My brothers had arrived home from work and after dinner we all three went back to Malvern and again combed the hills till ten o'clock, looking and calling, but sadly there was neither sight nor sound of Honey. My brother, Michael, who helped me a great deal with the dogs, travelling to all the shows and handling some of the dogs in the ring for me, asked me if I had contacted the Royal Society for the Prevention of Cruelty to Animals, or RSPCA as they were commonly known, to see if she had been reported to them. This was something I had not thought about so next morning I duly telephoned the local officer. I had heard that they sometimes trap animals in wire cages and thought this might be an idea. If Honey should still be in the area, perhaps we could entice her into a cage and thereby trap her.

'Yes,' said the RSPCA officer when I got through on the phone. He did have a trap but as it was the Royal Show on in Warwickshire he was there for the rest of the week so could do nothing till that was over. Don't worry about things, he would soon sort it out after the show. He would definitely recapture Honey for me as soon as we had found out where she was. I felt very cheered by this confident talk, felt here was someone who knew exactly what to do, which I certainly did not. My problems would soon be over. I also contacted the Malvern Ring Craft Club and found everybody very sympathetic. All the members said they would look out for her whenever they took their dogs for walks, not just over the hills but whenever they went out in any of the surrounding countryside.

In the next few days the newspaper advertisements were also starting to come out and consequently the phone started to ring with all sorts of helpful suggestions and tips. She had definitely been seen here, there and everywhere. I would dash out with Greta in the car as, although you can describe a Beardie to someone, Greta looked so like Honey, at that time, and the actual sight of a similar dog was far better as I soon found out. People took one look at Greta and said, 'Oh no, nothing like that. The one I saw looked like Lassie' – a Rough Collie, or a Border Collie or a Shaggy Mutt or anything but not like a Beardie at all. As I drove along I would look at every hillside or field just in case she might be trotting along trying to get home. You read all these stories of dogs travelling many miles to get home, sometimes footsore and weary, but home. I recalled the story of a Beardie called Clover who, when only about ten months old, on her way to ring craft classes, had been involved in a car accident. Her mistress had been badly injured and the dog had been thrown clean out of the car and had disappeared. The owner had been taken to hospital and no one could find the dog anywhere. She had vanished, bolted in terror as Honey had done for me. A couple of days later the bitch turned up on her own doorstep, somewhat dirty and dishevelled but none the worse for her ordeal. She had never done the trip to the classes except in the car so did not have any knowledge of the route which she would have, had she walked it regularly.

Then there was the case of Standly. He was the son of one of my bitches and had been sold to a couple who had started breeding Beardies in London with the hope of him being a top show dog. Standly turned out to be just what they wanted and won Top Puppy and Top Junior in the breed. As Sue and Willie had only bitches at home, Standly went to live at Sue's sister's house 8 miles across London, the other side of Heathrow Airport, just about the busiest airport in the world. Standly, as he was growing up to be a such a super dog, soon started getting bitches visit him for stud. Sue and Willie would drive over to Sue's sister's house to collect Standly, bring him over to meet his lovely lady and usually return him home the same day. One dreadful afternoon, Sue had a telephone call from her sister to say Standly had vanished, someone had left the garden gate open and there was simply no sign of the dog. Immediately everyone jumped into cars and drove round the area for the rest of the afternoon and evening but no sign of the missing dog. Sue and Willie eventually returned home, after doing all the usual things such as informing the police and checking all the local dog pounds, and sadly went to bed. At three o'clock in the morning they were woken up by a dog bark, a somewhat imperious dog bark, which sounded as if it was at their front door. Willie rushed down to see if, by some mischance, one of their bitches had managed to get to the front of the house. He opened the door and standing on the doorstep was a rather tired and slightly dishevelled Standly who immediately marched in and went for a long drink from the dogs' water dish. He then had a quick look round to find the expected lady-friend that he had obviously deluded himself he would find ready and waiting for him. On not finding her, and being really rather tired, he promptly went to sleep. Willie took him back to his own home the next day. That naughty dog decided to repeat the trip again some several weeks later arriving again on Sue and Willie's doorstep some hours after, this time, jumping the gate to get out. He had not only skirted Heathrow Airport but had had to cross the A4, one of the busiest roads out of London to the west. He had only been driven in a car along the route so must have worked it all out by smell. Needless to say, after the second escapade he did not return to Sue's sister's house but remained in, what was obviously, the home he preferred.

On remembering these two tales I wondered if perhaps my puppy would one day manage to return home herself. I would open the house door every morning hoping against hope I might see Honey sitting there, tail wagging, asking to be let in and have her dinner. However, there were several things against my finding her there. Honey was several months younger then either of these animals. She also had a main river to cross, the Severn, one of England's bigger rivers in the Worcester area, a main railway line and a longer distance to travel – 20 miles against Standly's 8 and Clover's 4 or 5.

So there I was continuing to travel round, driving up and down any road or track, walking up the hills still calling and looking but sadly with no sight or sound of Honey. The days were passing and the vet had only given Honey a week to survive. I was beginning to get slowly more convinced she must be dead. One day, I was driving along one road when I suddenly saw something gently flapping in the breeze in a ditch. It almost looked like Honey's long coat blowing in the wind. My heart gave a lurch. Was this how I was going to find her, dead in a ditch? I stopped the car and leapt out but it was only a paper-bag caught up in the weeds. I was so relieved. So long as she hadn't been found dead there was still a chance she was alive and coping somewhere.

It must have been about a week after Honey had disappeared when the phone rang, once again, 'I think I have seen your missing dog on the Malverns,' a voice said.

I asked him to describe her and this time it really did sound as if it was the right dog. The man ringing was living in the centre of Malvern and was working at the local radar works as an observer. He had a marvellous telescope for watching the birds on the hills from the lounge of his flat and had seen the article on Honey's loss in the local newspaper so had been keeping an eye open for her. He had seen her wandering along a path, about two-thirds of the way up the hills, each evening for a couple of nights at about six or six-thirty, after the majority of the visitors to the hills had left for their meals and everything had gone quiet. As where he had seen Honey was very near to where she had bolted, this sounded very hopeful indeed.

I said I would rush straight over but he, very sensibly, said no, wait. It was no good during the day as he never saw her earlier. If I got there about six he would look out for her and then take me up to the spot where she went regularly. He gave me his telephone number in case I would need to contact him and we arranged to meet at the carpark where the path up to Saint Anne's Well started. I took Greta as usual, just to make quite sure it really was Honey this time. We met as arranged. When Tony, as that was his name, saw Greta he said that she was exactly the same as the dog he had been seeing on the hills and, yes, he had seen her as usual just before he had left his flat to meet me. He thought she had been limping a bit tonight though, which worried me a bit. We immediately started the climb up the hills to get there before Honey should disappear, with me very hopeful that at last my quest would be over and I would have Honey safely home by that evening. We passed Saint Anne's Well with its restaurant and drinking-fountain and soon were walking along the path on which Tony had seen Honey. We walked very quietly so as not to frighten her away and, as we walked round the ridge and into the valley, there she was at the far end. She saw us at the same second and rapidly, even before I could call her, disappeared round the far ridge and vanished from sight. I immediately called her name but the wind was against us and I doubt if she could have heard it. We both ran round the valley as quickly as we could but there was no sight of Honey anywhere. It was as if she had never been there at all.

It was all very disappointing. So near and yet so far but at least we had some progress. Honey was still alive. She had not been limping as Tony had suspected. She had obviously found both food and water so was coping. No one had shot her and no one had captured or stolen her. If she had stayed so very close to the area where she had initially disappeared, maybe she might stay in the same area for a bit longer, making recapture somewhat easier. Things were definitely looking up.

I had not heard a word from the RSPCA officer and thought he must be back from the Royal Show by now. He had sounded so positive and now we had found Honey he would surely be able to catch her very rapidly for me. Tony and I, after spending the usual time walking and calling her name with no further sight of Honey, abandoned the hills and retraced our footsteps down to the carpark calling in at Saint Anne's Well tearoom on the way. I asked if they had seen Honey but they said, no, they had not seen any sign of her but had noticed the litter bins tipped upside down every morning for several days now. They had put it down to foxes but now realised it was most likely Honey scavenging for food. She was more used to bits of bread or ice cream than a fox would be so she was probably eating sufficiently from the scraps of food left in the bins to at least sustain life, and she could get water from the drinking-fountain. Although I had never seen any streams or troughs of water, with all the sheep on the hills there had got to be water easily available for both sheep and Honey. She had survived for ten days now; she had lived through the first and worst part of her ordeal. She could obviously manage for a little longer on her own.

A BONE TO TEMPT

Luckily, the weather continued to hold fair so I did not need to worry about Honey in bad weather. I hoped she would be able to find a snug nest in the bracken. As the RSPCA officer was now home, I rang him with great hopes. As we now had a fair idea of Honey's whereabouts, I was interested to find out how he intended to capture her for me. Those hopes were very soon dashed.

'Oh no,' said the voice on the end of the phone. 'You can borrow my trap cage if you like. Can you collect it today? I shall be away from tomorrow.'

There was no suggestion of how I was supposed to drag it up some very steep hills or how to site, set and bait it. I had to wait until my brothers returned home from work so we could all drive over to Malvern, collect the cage, which turned out to be large and very heavy, and struggle up the hills dragging the cage to the valley where I had seen Honey the previous evening.

There was not a lot of cover in this particular valley. There was a path which was fairly wide and ran round the middle of the hill. The only cover was a couple of scrubby trees about two-thirds of the way round the path, going from the Saint Anne's Well end. There were another four scrubby trees halfway down the slope towards the tree line which covered the lower path. This was the most popular of the walks, being easy with no hard climbs. I decided the best place for the cage would be near the four trees, halfway down the hillside, as putting it anywhere near the path would mean it being seen and either being messed about with by children or, at worst, disappearing completely which would not please the RSPCA man at all and it would certainly not result in Honey's capture. We dragged the cage the last distance to a flat bit of ground some 40 yards or so away from the trees. I did not want it directly under the trees as there was no bracken there and it was more likely to be seen or found. I also wanted to sit there to look out for Honey should she come, hoping I could still call her to me.

We covered the entire cage, including the floor, with thick bracken so she would not suspect a trap and also so that it might not be seen from above by other people walking along the path. We set the trap and left it. I had thought long and hard about baiting the trap. You needed something to tie to the wire at the far end, away from the door, which would tempt the animal you were trying to capture into grabbing the bait, pulling hard enough to release the door. That then snapped shut with the animal inside who would have to wait there until you released him (or in this case her) when you next visited the trap. Ordinary food could not be tied to the tripwire so I had bought a large juicy bone. Honey loved her bones and would certainly wish to take it back with her to her nest. Sheep, being herbivores, would not be interested in fresh meat and I would have to pray a fox would find the scent of man on the bone sufficient to discourage him helping himself and, therefore, springing the trap. Should that happen, one fox would have an unpleasant few hours before he was let free.

The other thing I now felt I must do was to feed Honey. I did not know how she was faring for food. She had obviously found a good water supply otherwise would not have still been alive. So, I decided I would take her food up and place it in the cage to tempt her inside. We tied the bone securely at the back of the cage, tested that when it was pulled the trap was sprung, and placed the food at the entrance to encourage her in. We then sat under the trees to wait for a while and see if Honey would appear.

Waiting is a bit of a boring game if you are not interested in nature. You cannot talk or move about as talking will be heard and any movement will be seen. Then the dog just will not come. I had to get her near enough to me for her to recognise both my voice and smell. If she just appeared over the distant hilltop and saw a person, she would disappear again before she was near enough to realise it was me. So, we sat there and enjoyed watching the birds till it started to get dark. I still had the dogs at home to feed and exercise and my brothers had to get up early for work the next day so, as there was no sign whatsoever of Honey, we left her the food at the entrance to the trap, with the bone nestling on its bed of bracken at the back, and left, all hopeful of going next day to see a naughty Beardie puppy sitting there, inside the trap, all secure and ready to go home.

My profession at that time was as a canine beautician. I would travel into Birmingham and trim dogs in their own homes, three days a week (Monday, Wednesday and Friday). I left the house after feeding and exercising my own dogs in the morning, about ten o'clock, and my last appointment was usually about seven in the evening. I did not start for home until eight o'clock, arriving back about forty-five minutes to one hour later, according to which area I finished up in. I was working in Birmingham the next day so decided I would drive straight to Malvern from Birmingham, rather than go home first, as to do that would have involved a large diversion and so make it very much later to finally arrive home. Thank goodness for light evenings. Being late June it was only dark for a few hours overnight so, consequently, off I went to Malvern as soon as the last dog was clipped, quite confident I would find Honey in the trap.

I parked as usual in the Clock Tower Carpark and climbed the increasingly familiar footpath up to where we had left the cage. I found it easily enough but was extremely disappointed to see it had not been touched. The bone was exactly as we had left it, at the back of the cage, and the food was also just sitting there. I stared at it all feeling very depressed. I had been so sure I would be bringing Honey home with me tonight and the last couple of weeks would just turn into a distant nightmare. Obviously, it was not going to be so easy to recapture her. I sat down on the grass by the cage and wondered what to do. Perhaps the scent of the cage was too strong and strange. I had better put the food slightly further away from it and, if I slowly regained her confidence and if we could tempt her to start eating again, work it slowly back towards the cage. I placed the food from yesterday about 6 feet away from the cage, on a small grassy slope, hidden well by the surrounding high bracken, and left the bone and cage primed to go off as before. She might be tempted to try for the bone after she had eaten the food. Hopefully!

I climbed dispiritedly back down the hill to my car and drove home to tell my expectant family there had been no sign of Honey, and no food had been taken. The next day, I went to Malvern, again with fresh food and thought I might try the Saint Anne's Well way up the hill. It might be a bit quicker. I was certainly getting very fit with all the trips up the hills and was managing to go faster and cut my time down quite a bit. I arrived at the cage to find the food had all gone. I was delighted and just hoped it was Honey that had eaten it all. I replaced it with the fresh food, about 3 inches nearer the cage. Leaving the cage, I walked to the

grassy spot under the trees and sat down to wait, yet again, for a couple of hours to see if Honey should appear so that I could call her to me. I was beginning to get concerned that she had been out for so long now, she might be becoming so wild that she would not come back to me anyway, so I decided to bring Barberry with me on my next trip. Barberry was a very good dog as, although she had not actually been trained, she would go and fetch back any dog which I commanded her to do. All I had to do was to say to Barberry 'Fetch Honey' or 'Fetch Angus' and she would immediately gallop off, communicate with the required dog and both dogs would come at once. Even if Honey did not come too near, I could send Barberry off after her and hopefully, this dog that she knew well would return her confidence sufficiently for her to come back with Barberry near enough to me for her to recognise me.

As I sat and debated these things in my mind, I suddenly saw a small brown shape come trotting down the hill from the top. Honey was using the sheep as cover. They never even lifted their heads as she slipped through them. My heart leapt. I am going to get her? flashed through my mind as I froze to immobility, praying for her to continue to come on towards me. Suddenly she stopped dead, looked towards the far end of the path where I saw, to my horror, a couple of people come round the bend and start to walk towards us. Honey just turned back up the hill and, slipping between the sheep, disappeared in a second. I don't know when I have felt so disappointed. Nevertheless, I sat there for another couple of hours in the vain hope that she might reappear but there was no further sign of her that evening and eventually, I had to give up my wait and return home. This was the start of many hours sitting and waiting under those trees for a sight of Honey. I decided I would need to feed her every day in the hope of keeping her well. I could not know how much of the food

she would be getting – any other animal wandering the hills might be eating it instead. The food I was feeding my dogs on, at the time, was a prepared frozen meat-and-tripe mix, already cooked. I bought it in frozen blocks and after thawing, would chop it up for the dogs. I didn't really think foxes, who would be the most likely to help themselves, would take it but the birds, such as magpies and crows, could be tempted. I would just have to trust to luck that Honey might get a bit at least, and so not starve to death at any rate. Everyday I climbed the hills and put her new food down. It was always in the evening as that was the time she came out, when the hills were quiet and all the people had gone home for tea. I would replace the food about 3 inches nearer the cage and I regularly replaced the bone, always leaving it tied to the spring in the trap. The food was always gone so I slowly began to get hopeful again. Barberry and I would sit under the now very familiar trees and silently watch the hills for any sign of the little brown figure. One evening, I saw her come round the bend of the far side of the valley, trotting along the path but once again she suddenly turned and went back the way she had come.

Eventually, the food was up to the cage. I would place it inside. Just inside, I thought. I mustn't frighten her off again. If I could only tempt her to put a foot inside, maybe it would work. They caught foxes in these cages and they were totally wild animals, not pet dogs. I left the food and went home that night wondering how I would find things the next day. Sadly, the food had not been touched when I arrived the following evening. There it lay, just inside the cage, exactly as I had left it. I put fresh food just outside the cage and returned home in the hope that she would take it from there again but, on returning the next day, the food had not been touched once more. The only thing to do was to start once again, with placing the food about 6 feet away and work it slowly forward each day, trusting that, as time went on, her confidence would increase and we still might tempt her inside and so catch her.

As you might expect, all the other Beardie owners knew of my loss. There was another show-going owner, called John, who lived with his family in Malvern. He had, obviously, been looking out for Honey but had never seen her. He now very kindly offered, when he heard I was feeding her every day, to go up and feed her on Sundays. I jumped at his offer. It would at least give me one-day-a-week break. John said he always took his own dog up the hills every weekend when he wasn't at work so it was no trouble to place a bit of food out at the same time. We met on a Saturday and I showed him where I had the cage hidden and where to put the food. We decided to sort out a hidy-hole that I would place Sunday's food in, on Saturday. John would then collect it on Sunday on his walk, and take it up the hills to be put out for Honey and then let me know if he had seen her. He never did. I suppose it was because he went up usually Sunday mornings, a busy time of day for hikers and picnic parties.

Slowly, slowly, I worked the food back to the mouth of the cage. It was still disappearing every night but once again, immediately I put the food into the mouth of the cage, it was still sitting there the next evening, untouched. I was sure it was Honey eating the food by now and it was beginning to look as if we were not going to tempt her inside. I would have to start to plan another method of capture if the cage idea was not going to work. I thought vaguely of the films I had seen of wild animals being shot by darts and dropping in a couple of seconds, all doped and ready to pick up. What about that for Honey? That idea was soon abandoned. Even though animals you see in the films keel over almost instantaneously, that, it appears, does not happen in real life. The anaesthetic in the darts can take up to a minute to work and a dog running flat out can go a long way in that time. We were very near the quarry on the hills, a sheer drop of several hundred feet. A dog running in terror, and with the anaesthetic starting to work so she would not really know what she was doing, could easily go straight over the edge. Forget that idea, I told myself.

But what about tracking her? Police dogs are trained to track. Perhaps I could have her tracked, get near enough to call her and get her back that way. The local police ran the Alcester Obedience School for Dogs so they would be the nearest ones to contact. I found out the evening that the classes were held and went along to find out if they could help. There were two sergeants there the evening I went and they listened very sympathetically to my story. Yes, they were both dog handlers but the dogs, that were actually trained police dogs, could not be used for the very simple reason that a dog is trained to track only man, therefore he will only work to a man track. If you ask him to track a dog, such as Honey, next time he is asked to track a man again he could get diverted from his man track to another dog track and so lose his use to his master. Oh dear, there goes another good idea – or maybe not. Both sergeants had pet dogs, not used for police work, and they were also trained to track. They would be only too happy to come to Malvern with me to try with a couple of their dogs. They would even enjoy a trip up the Malvern Hills. I was delighted, perhaps this would work.

We arranged for them to meet me in the Clock Tower Carpark at four on the Saturday afternoon. I left Barberry at home this time. I did not want to distract the new dogs from their job with a strange bitch to give them other ideas. I drove to Malvern that day, complete with the usual two meals. I was beginning to make sure I had the food in case it was needed should Honey not be recaptured. No point in having to return twice because we had failed again. My heart sank as the two policemen arrived just a few minutes after me. They had brought the family as well as the dogs and both had a couple of children with them. How on earth were children going to sit silently for perhaps a couple of hours, never mind trying to keep the dogs quiet and still too? Still, it was no good abandoning the idea before we had given it a try. So, we all trooped up the hill. I placed the food out and we all sat on the path, under the small trees, to wait. Needless to say, the children soon were running about, everyone chatted and the dogs enjoyed playing with the children. There was absolutely no chance whatsoever that we would see hide or hair of Honey that evening. After about an hour I said I thought we had better call it off and perhaps think of something else. The two sergeants said they had had a lovely afternoon and were sorry they hadn't managed to get Honey for me. Perhaps we could try again sometime, to which I said, 'Thank you very much, I will be in touch.' and once again, drove home, very dispiritedly.

KATE'S ENCOURAGING NEWS

Whilst I was busy clipping dogs, I would quite often mention Honey to my clients. When they were the last of the day's work I would, on leaving them, dash over to Malvern to put her food out. One lady, a Mrs Gray, who had bought a Poodle from me and had become a good friend, had a cottage in Wales which they went to regularly for holidays. Mrs Gray, in her turn, had told her old gardener in Wales all about Honey. She was sure he would have her in a day, without any trouble. He would snare her, Mrs Gray told me. What a brilliant idea. Would Mrs Gray bring him back with her on her next trip? I could take him up to Malvern, show him the set-up we had there and hope he could work something out. Of course Mrs Gray was only too happy to help and would ring me with news as soon as she had any.

The next time I trimmed Kiki, Mrs Gray's Poodle, I asked how things were progressing. Sadly, the old gardener had never left Wales. He had never travelled more than a few miles from his cottage in his life and just would not leave. I offered to go down and collect him and take him back the same day if he could only manage to catch Honey that quickly, but he would not budge. So, another plan had to be abandoned but the seed of an idea was sown in my mind and was to be of great use in the future, even though I did not realise it at the time.

With several dogs and bitches producing puppies you get to know your vet very well. I had told Mr Geddes, my vet, all about my loss. It was he who had told me that when a dog is lost they usually do not run for miles and miles non-stop, as I had feared, but, once the initial bolt calms down, will usually stay in that area and make the surroundings home. They can move, of course, and extend their hunting ground and, should their nest be disturbed, move to another area but it was the same as staying around your own house; the nest is home. Honey certainly proved him right in her behaviour, staying very near to where I had lost her.

The next idea I came up with was how about trying to dope her. If she would take some dope and stay near the food for long enough for it to sedate her, perhaps I could get her before she disappeared. I asked Mr Geddes for something that would work in this manner. He gave me some small yellow pills. 'Put three of these in her food. They will not harm her but make her very wobbly on her legs, so she will not then be able to run away so fast. You should be able to capture her then. They will also act as a tranquilliser to calm her fears and make her less liable to try and dash off,' he said. I decided to go fairly late at night and be prepared to spend the night up there. I would have to wait for Honey to come and goodness knows what time she was coming these days for her food. I would, as always, take Barberry with me. My mother, who was not keen on my being on my own I suspect, said she would come as well. So, at about ten o'clock that night, we went on the now very familiar route to Malvern, with food, dope and warm clothing as, although it was beautiful weather, the nights did go rather chilly if you were sitting out.

We climbed the hills and I put out the dope in some

crunchy biscuits. I felt the pills would melt into the meat and so flavour the whole lot. Honey might dislike the taste and ignore it which would invalidate the whole project. We decided to stay on the path that night, so we were well away from the cage and food. Hopefully, Honey would not smell us and be put off. I also wanted her to remain nearby so the dope, which would take about 20 minutes to work, had time to start sedating her before she decided to move off. There were a lot of ifs and buts in the whole idea but it was worth a try. Nothing else had worked and I felt I was prepared to try anything by now. It was a beautiful night; the moon was shining, making everything look like a fairyland. The lights of the town of Malvern below us winked in the deeper dark of the land and trees, and the sounds travelled up so clearly we could hear virtually every word that was spoken, even though the people were speaking several hundred feet below.

We only saw one couple walking over the hills. They came round the bend of the hill in the same place that I had seen Honey come round some weeks previously. We heard voices first, then they appeared. They came forward a few steps, then they stopped. They must have seen us sitting on the path or, at least and more likely, have seen Barberry's white shirt-front gleaming in the moonlight. Both myself and my mother were in coats and dark clothing so probably not visible. Whether they thought Barberry was a spirit of the hills or not, they rapidly turned and went back the way they had come. I would have loved to have known what they said to each other on the way back down the hill.

So we sat on, undisturbed. The sounds of human habitation slowly died down in the town below and by about one o'clock everything became very quiet indeed. Just the sounds of the night-birds and animals to keep us company. Slowly, the hours slipped by with no sign of Honey whatsoever. Dawn came very early at that time of year, at around three-thirty in fact. Just before the coming of dawn, the night which had been pleasantly cool, suddenly became rather chilly and I discovered to my horror, a thick mist slowly swirling up the valley. Soon it was eddying all around us. There was no way I could see Honey come or go. Perhaps it would disappear as quickly as it had come. It was also getting very chilly indeed. We sat on for another half an hour in the hopes the mist would disappear. Things had gone very silent and suddenly I heard the distinct sound of biscuits being crunched up. What should I do? Dare I go down and see if I could spot Honey? I was sure that long before I could see her she would hear me coming and bolt. The best thing to do would be to sit and wait a little bit longer and hope she would stay near the food, get drowsy and lie down to sleep. Then, with the dope working, I would hopefully get near enough before she would try and rush off. We waited about half an hour. I crept down to the food and looked around in the hopes of seeing a stretched-out, fast-asleep dog, lying by her biscuits.

I needn't have crept. There was neither sight or sound of her. I looked all round the area: in the bracken, under the trees, nothing. I climbed back up to the path and said to my mother and Barberry, 'We might as well go home.' This idea was once again a failure. Honey was still loose and probably fast asleep, tucked up in her nest, wherever it was. She, at least, would be getting a good night's rest.

We drove home, arriving about seven-thirty, just in time for breakfast. 'You are up early,' my grandmother said as I took her a cup of tea. I didn't really feel like telling her we had spend the night sitting on the Malvern Hills.

Thorne Dene, the house where I lived at the time, had been an old farmhouse; so old, in fact, that it had been mentioned in the Doomsday Book. It had been extended regularly over the years of course, but the coal-house was definitely the oldest part with the kitchen and pantry still very old and the front having been modernised about 150 years ago. When we first moved in, we discovered it was haunted but as it had the most marvellously peaceful atmosphere and was a very friendly house, none of us were concerned about the resident spirits. In fact, we had made contact with them. My best friend in the village, a girl called Mona who lived in an ancient cottage which was also haunted, had, one evening, for a bit of fun, told me all about ouija boards and how to contact spirits through them. You do not need to go to all the expense or difficulty of finding a shop to sell you one. All you need is a small well-polished table, an upturned empty wineglass, some paper on which you write all the letters of the alphabet, numerals (zero through to nine) and the words Yes and No. Cut out all your letters etc. into small separate squares and place in alphabetical order, then the numerals and finally the Yes and No in a large circle on your polished table. Do leave as much of a space as possible in between the individual pieces of paper to avoid mixing up which one you are going to receive from the spelling. You will then need possibly three people sitting round the table, each with a finger, preferably the forefinger, placed very lightly on the base of the upturned glass. There is no need to sit in the dark or make any other preparations. One person can do it on their own as my brother found out when he decided to have a go. One of the most important things to remember is never to use it for gain, only as interest in the past or, as I used it, to try and trace someone. We had tried it first, to find out who was haunting Thorne Dene. I was extremely sceptical about the whole thing and was sure someone was pushing the glass. We sat around the small table: my two brothers, John and Michael, my mother and myself with questions, having read ghost stories before, like 'Is there anyone there?' Nothing. We

44

asked again and very slowly the glass started to revolve in clockwise movements inside the circle of letters. It then slowly went over to the word Yes. We then asked who it was and, slowly but with increasing speed, the glass moved first to the letter K then to A followed by T and finally E. It then went back to the middle and stopped. The movement was very definite but I was still convinced someone was pushing the glass.

We decided to ask various different questions and discovered Kate had lived at Thorne Dene in around AD 1500, and the person we had all heard stomping about upstairs in the old part of the house, was Sarah Laughern. They had both stayed at Thorne Dene because they had loved it so much which was one of the reasons why the house had such a happy atmosphere. I still thought someone was pushing the glass but no one had ever heard mention of the name Sarah Laughern. Perhaps John had made it up and pushed the glass to make it interesting. My youngest sister, Sally Ann, who was staying with us at the time, went up the next day and walked round the churchyard with her current boyfriend from Portsmouth. When she returned she said she had found a gravestone there with the name Sarah Laughern who had died in the late eighteen-hundreds. As I knew none of us had known anything about either Kate or Sarah beforehand, I began to think perhaps there was more to this than met the eye.

Prior to losing Honey, we had built up quite a good contact with Kate and she would come very quickly when we put the table and bits of paper out. We always used the same wineglass and, on the occasional time we got another spirit, we would say goodbye and leave it at once. After the failure of the night's escapade and the fact that I hadn't seen Honey for some time now, although her food was still being taken every night but never when it was too near the cage, I had rather given up any hope of ever getting her in the trap. Then I suddenly thought of asking Kate where Honey was hiding. Would she be able to help at all?

That evening, when we were all in, John got out the glass and bits of paper and arranged them correctly on the small coffee-table we always used. I opened out a large Ordnance Survey map of the Malverns. It would be much quicker to just point to a spot and get a Yes or No than have it all spelt out. Kate arrived in the glass very fast. Sometimes we had to wait for several minutes for her to come but not tonight. We asked if she knew we had lost Honey, Yes came back at once. Did she know where Honey was? Yes. Slowly we pointed to spot after spot, all round the area of the cage and every time the answer came back No. So we started to move along the length of the hills towards British Camp. Suddenly, almost at British Camp, the glass flew over to Yes. It was so definite I felt Kate must be right. I then asked the question uppermost in my mind: 'Was Honey well and would I get her back?' We immediately had the answer Yes to both. We thanked Kate for her help, said 'God be with you' which was always her way of signing off, and put the glass and letters back into the cabinet where we always kept them. That night I went to bed with a lighter heart than I had for several weeks.

The following day, when I went up to Malvern, I took her food and placed it in the usual spot then walked down to the bottom path and followed it round to the spot where Kate had said Honey was. Once again, I called and called as I walked. Barberry thought this was a better walk than the usual one of sitting still for hours and I almost expected to see Honey trotting down the path in front of me, so high were my expectations. Needless to say, I did not and, after about an hour of combing the area, I had to abandon it again and go home.

The months were slipping by and summer was changing to autumn. the nights were getting colder and Honey was still loose. I racked my brain for any other ideas of how to get her back. Then, one day, the phone rang and a lady's voice on the other end of the line said, 'Are you the person who has lost a dog on the Malverns?' After such a long time I was very surprised to get a new lead but said at once, 'Yes I am.'

'Have you recovered the dog yet?' came the query.

'No, I know she is still around but so far still free.'

'I think I know where she is,' said the voice. I at once asked for details of who she was and where she lived and jumped in the car to go and find out more. The house was a farm cottage in a village called Guarlford, at the far end of the Malvern Hills range and just below the area Kate had said Honey was. What had happened was the lady had an aunt who had an aged Poodle which she regularly had to take to the vet. One day, the aunt was visiting and Father, who was the cowman on the farm, in conversation mentioned that he hadn't seen his little dog that morning. It was always with the cows when he got them in for milking in the morning. 'What dog?' the daughter said.

'Oh, it's just a shaggy dog, she sits up on the bank with the cows and I have seen her for the last few weeks nearly every morning. She doesn't do anything, just slips away when the cows go down for milking.'

'Just a minute,' says the aunt. ' I remember seeing a notice on the vet's board in the waiting-room about a lost dog. It's been there for some months and there's a big reward.' That was what made the daughter's ears prick up. It certainly couldn't do any harm to ring up and find out, which is what they did. So I arrived at the farm with Greta, again, to find out if it could possibly be Honey.

Father was there when I arrived. 'Oh yes, it looks just like that one,' he said, looking at Greta. So Kate was right. Honey had moved. She would have liked the company of the cows as we were surrounded by cattle at Thorne Dene and she had regularly been exercised through fields of cows since she was very young. The farm would be much quieter than the hills with no tourists walking all over to disturb her. I went straight over to the farm and had a word with the farmer as this farm was too far out for my initial tour of the farms of the area. Yes, he had also seen Honey, several times, and had meant to shoot her as a loose dog and a menace. But luckily for both Honey and myself, he had never had his gun on him when he saw her. I asked if we could walk over his land to try and get her back and to please, not shoot her. She definitely would not harm anything. She would have done it before now if she had had the inclination. The farmer was most sympathetic saying Yes to everything so, whilst I was there, I decided to take a walk round the farm and see if I could spot her myself.

There were bits of Beardie hair in several spots, stuck in the barbed wire where she had obviously been travelling over the farm. She definitely was making the farm her home. I decided it would be much better to feed her here now, rather than by the cage as I realised she was travelling a fair distance every day for her food and the journey involved crossing both a busy main road and, even worse, a main railway line. She could easily be killed on either of those. It was a miracle that so far, she had survived both. There seemed to be one spot where there was more Beardie hair hanging on the wire than other places and the cows were not in the field on the one side so I placed the food slightly to one side of the empty field's fence and prayed she might find it there. I went the next day to find the majority of the food still there; obviously magpies or crows had been tucking in but not Honey. On the second day the food was all gone. It looked as if Honey had found it.

I saw the cowman walking over the farm and decided to have a chat with him. Honey was growing up, there was a good chance she had come into season. she could easily have been mated by a farm collie from any of the farms in the area and maybe even have whelped and be nursing a litter. I asked the cowman if he could keep an eye and an ear open whilst he was walking over the farm, for any sign or sound of puppies. Young puppies can be very noisy little beasts in their play, growling and yapping to each other. They would not keep quiet as their mum had learnt to do, so should this very undesirable event have occurred, at least we should be able to trace Honey's nest and recapture her and her unwanted family. Mr Jones agreed and told me later he had walked the entire farm, checking every hedgerow, nook and cranny but had found nothing.

Beardies have excellent noses. I had often watched my dogs track either myself or other members of my family, or each other. Many's the time I have walked round the orchard and on the way back have one of the dogs go past me, nose glued to the ground, following my track with such concentration that they pass me by within a couple of feet not even aware they are so near. Sometimes, I have let them complete the track until they go all over the ground you have covered and turn up where you are standing, all pleased with themselves, tails wagging, or I have called them as they pass you by, intent on the trail. They then look all confused and come up to you looking somewhat sheepish as if to say 'Silly me, passing you by'. I wondered, with such excellent ability, could one of the dogs track Honey and lead me to her? Angus was about five years old then. Old enough to be sensible, young enough to be keen and was the one who seemed to have the greatest desire to do tracking. Let's take Angus and have a go.

Now we had found Honey on the farm, I saw her fairly often. I suppose the farm was so much quieter than the hills, very few people around at all so she probably felt easier and more relaxed. She would still slip away, just trotting quietly like a fox does, never in a blind panic blundering and galloping in a mad frenzy but calm and quiet like a wraith in the night. So the next day, Angus and Barberry were popped in the car for the daily trip to Malvern and, complete with Honey's food for that day, off we went. I parked as usual in the farmyard and took the two dogs over the fields towards the usual feeding spot. I sometimes went through a small orchard, as a different route, rather than the quickest way which was through the fields and cows. As I opened the orchard gate, there at the far end, was Honey. Was my luck in at last? She stopped dead on seeing me and the two dogs. I grabbed Angus's collar and said in a low voice, 'There's Honey. Find Honey.' He wagged his tail and, as I was about to let him go, Honey vanished through the hedge as silently and quietly as if she had never been there. Angus streaked across the orchard and then started to scent her. He followed her track into the next field and for a fair distance across it, but he had never been trained in the art of tracking and soon lost it and I could not get him to continue. He just could not work out what I wanted, so we ended up going to place the food in the usual spot and returning home. Yet another idea proved to be of no use.

The idea was not a complete waste though as another thought followed on from the idea of tracking. Perhaps I could get the two police sergeants back. Honey was in a smaller area now. Perhaps it could be easier to find her. If I could persuade the chaps to only bring one dog each, and no children, try doping Honey again and then track her with trained dogs, we might get her. I went along to the obedience class they held on Tuesday nights and found them both there instructing. I told them of the progress we had had and how Honey had moved. Then I mentioned my new plan. They had, obviously, realised the previous try

had been rather fruitless and agreed to just come themselves and bring a dog each.

We arranged to meet at my house and go on together in one car. At five o'clock, on the appointed afternoon, we loaded the car, two dogs, Honey's food and dope, and drove to Guarlford. The road was by now becoming as familiar as the road to Malvern had been but at least I didn't have very steep hills to climb any more. We put the, by now doped food in the usual spot and crept away to a safe distance to wait for her to come and take it. For once, she obliged and came into view after we had been waiting for only about an hour. We all sat extremely quiet, including the dogs who had their muzzles held very firmly to prevent them barking.

Honey polished off her food and mooched around for several minutes then sat down and looked as if she might even be deciding to curl up and go to sleep. Good, it looked as if things were working out to plan. Then a sudden loud noise from several fields away disturbed everyone. Honey jumped up and started to trot away. We also moved. The police put their dogs on to Honey's scent and we started quietly to follow her. She saw us coming on behind her and flew over a five-barred gate and disappeared into a field of sheep. The sheep did not even lift a head to look at her. Good, we all thought, the dope is starting to take effect and she must have dropped down to go to sleep. We stood and waited for her to become more sedated then walked quietly into the field. We combed the field from one end to the other. There was absolutely no sign of Honey, whatsoever. She had completely vanished. We had seen her go into the field and drop down on to her stomach, and we presumed she had gone to sleep. What she must have done was to crawl along on her stomach throughout the entire length of the field, without even one ewe or lamb turning its head to watch her crawl by, until she got out of the field. She had used the sheep on the Malverns to hide behind as she slipped away. I had seen her do that several times but to crawl through an entire flock and vanish! I did not think any dog could be so clever.

We tried to track her with the trained dogs. We walked over a great deal of the farm but the dogs did not seem to be able to find, or be interested in, her tracks as we must have crossed them many times. In the end, we decided we had better all go home and call it a day. Once again, another idea abandoned. I just could not believe how Honey, as we well knew, had eaten a large amount of dope which had had time to take effect as she had been snoozing and messing about around her meal, could still jump a five-barred gate and be sufficiently aware to crawl through the sheep and disappear.

I saw Mr Geddes, the vet, and asked him how on earth it could happen. 'Mind over matter,' was his reply. She was obviously a dog of great intelligence. She must have survived quite a few very difficult and dangerous situations and learnt how to disappear or extricate herself from whatever position she found herself in. With this thought in mind, I decided it was a complete waste of time to try any more attempts at doping her. Obviously we would never get her back that way.

THE FINAL RESORT

At the time, my best friend was Mona. She was a great horsewoman as was her husband, Micky, who was the joint master of the local Hunt. Mona and I had regularly ridden out together when I had my horses, which I gave up when I started to show the dogs again. I found there was just not enough time to ride and attend to five horses, plus show and breed dogs. So, the horses were all sold and I concentrated on the dogs. I still would go for a pleasant ride with Mona every so often, borrowing one of her horses. I had, long ago, told her about losing Honey and she regularly asked if I had managed to get her back. We were out riding one day, when Mona happened to mention something about a chap who could snare foxes. Snare foxes! My ears pricked up at once. The old chap from Wales had said he could have snared Honey for me. This chap was local, how about trying him? I asked Mona if she would talk to him about it. 'Of course,' came back the reply. 'It's worth a try.'

I waited very impatiently for several days but heard nothing from Mona so, as I could not contain my impatience any longer, decided to ring her. She had asked Micky to ring him which he had now done. Mr France was not interested at all as it was a dog. No way was he going to catch a dog and, as far as he was concerned, the matter ended there. My hopes were all dashed once again. I seemed to be hitting my head against a brick wall – every single thing that I had thought of had failed. Honey had outwitted my every dodge and trick. She was so near. I saw her so regularly. I just could not get any nearer to capturing her. She might as well be lost completely and never be seen again, such was my present dilemma. The worst thing was summer had turned to autumn and that was rapidly changing into winter. We had had a beautiful Indian summer but we were now getting to the end of October. Honey was nearing her first birthday and, if she had not yet been in season, it could only be a very short time before she was. She definitely had not had a litter yet, thank heavens, but how long did we have left?

Barberry had come back into season after I lost Honey and, as Cairnbhan was getting older now, and I did not know if I would ever get Honey back, I had decided to mate Barberry back to Cairnbhan to get the same breeding, before it would become impossible due to Cairnbhan's age. Barberry was due to whelp in the early part of November. One day, as I came back from trimming in Birmingham, I went over to feed Honey as usual. The weather was dreadful, pouring rain. The nights were drawing in fast and I had a sudden desperate feeling that I had to get her back, fast. I struggled back to the car through the mud and rain. As soon as I arrived home I rang Mona. Luckily she was in. I asked her for the name and address of the chap who snared foxes. As she did not have either herself, she consulted Micky and obtained both for me, as well as directions to his house. I thought I would go in person. I would not just ring up when he could say No! easily. I would speak to him face to face and beg him to have a go. At least, nothing ventured, nothing gained, so to speak.

Back into the car and off I drove, praying that as it was such a rotten night, he would be in. As I was driving up his

55

drive, joy! I saw the lights were on in the house. Mr France himself came to the door and asked me in. I felt the best plan would be to tell him the story right from the beginning and try and get his sympathy, rather than just a bald 'can you trap my dog?' approach, which he probably had from Micky and promptly said No to. Mr France listened sympathetically to my story and asked exactly where she was. I described the farm at Guarlford and established that he knew the area.

'Please,' I said. 'Please, I cannot leave her out for the winter. I must get her back.'

'You realise,' said Mr France, 'the only way I can get her is by snaring. I have a cage but it's up in Scotland and will not be available for a couple of months. With snaring, she can strangle herself before I can release her and then all you will have returned is a dead dog!'

'I appreciate that, and am prepared to take the risk. I cannot let her die slowly from starvation, or be shot [either of which could happen at any time]. She has managed to survive this long by sheer luck,' I replied.

'Right,' he said, 'my terms are by the hour. I would like to meet you at the farm to see the layout on Wednesday evening, providing the weather is fine.'

Suddenly my heart lightened. He had agreed. This time it had got to work. I drove home with more hope in my heart than I had had for several weeks and, on going to bed, prayed for fine weather for Wednesday so we would not be delayed again. My prayers must have been answered as Wednesday developed into a beautiful day. I met Mr France at the appointed time at the farm gate. I had Honey's dinner with me to show him where I usually fed her. As we walked briskly across the fields, towards the feeding spot, I suddenly saw Honey at the edge of the field we were just entering. I grabbed Mr France's arm to restrain him without speaking and pointed

Honey out with just a whispered 'There she is. That's Honey.'

Mr France, being a countryman and used to the ways of wild animals, as that is surely what Honey was by now, just acknowledged by pointing a finger.

Then Honey got up and stretched, scented us and steadily, with no hurry, trotted off and disappeared, just as a fox would do, quite unconcerned. But there was no way we could get near enough to do anything about it. As Honey's tail vanished after her, we continued across the field, and the next one, and ended up at the spot in the fence where I was placing the food each night. Mr France looked at the fence and surrounding area. 'Yes,' he said, 'this is an ideal spot to place the snare.' We could see from the wisps of coat where her regular passage was through the barbed wire. That would be a perfect position to tie and set the snare. 'Give me the food, I will set it out tonight to leave my scent. Then we will starve her tomorrow to get her really hungry and I will come out again on Friday morning, lay some food and try to catch her.'

Mr France's plan was to come out at about seven on Friday morning and, after laying a bit of food in the usual place, set the snare. I had previously told him the cowman still saw Honey, nearly every morning, around eight. Just as he would call the cows in for milking, she would do her disappearing act so we felt fairly confident that, with no food for a couple of days, she would probably be checking her usual food spot pretty regularly. By then, she would be getting fairly peckish. We both drove home. I felt in my heart this time it would work. It was so wonderful to have another person who seemed to have more ideas to help. My family had been marvellous but we had all run out of new suggestions and everything we had tried had failed.

I woke up on Friday morning to find it was again pouring with really heavy rain. There was no way Honey would come out today. She never did like rain. Even as a tiny puppy she had to be taken out and made to stay to do her jobs and, as soon as she had finished, would rush back into the house to get warm and dry again. She had obviously found herself a good nest and would be staying in until the weather improved. Friday was one of my days in Birmingham. It was one of the longest days I have ever had. I had arranged to ring Mr France in the evening to hear how he had got on so drove home very fast indeed. I rang as soon as I got through the door. Mr France was back at home. 'No,' he said. He had arrived at seven as planned, set the snare and laid out a bit of food, returned to where he could not be seen and sat and waited. Just as I had suspected, no sign whatsoever of Honey. At nine-thirty, a very wet Mr France decided it was pretty pointless to stay any longer, collected his snare and went back home to dry out. He would go again next morning, Saturday, and hope for better luck.

I had a couple of dogs entered at a show in South Wales the following day. Michael and I bathed and prepared the dogs for the show. As always, it was a job to be done the night before a show. I suggested to Michael that he had better go on his own as I really thought I could not be away for a full day in case Mr France managed to get Honey. 'Fine,' replied my brother. He regularly handled the dogs, especially Crofter, who was one of the two to go, and Cardiff was not a long run. Michael went off early as you need to be at a show for about eight-thirty.

I knew it wasn't any good ringing or doing anything until about nine or ten. Mr France could still be waiting for Honey to come out. If or when he had caught her, he would have to drive home, taking about half an hour. By nine-thirty, however, I could contain myself no longer. I would have to ring and find out if he was back and what had happened. After all the rain of the previous day,

Saturday was a simply glorious morning. Surely he would have a chance today. The phone seemed to ring for ages then, at last, was answered. Mr France was on the other end of the line. He had just driven in and heard it ringing.

'Yes,' he said, 'I have your dog. She came out and went for her food just as we had planned it.'

'Is she OK?' I asked in fear and trembling, having a sudden dread that the snare had done its work too well and she had been strangled before Mr France had released her.

'Fine,' he replied. She had bitten at his wellingtons as he undid the restraining knot, but that was all.

'She has,' he said, 'sat quietly in the back of my van all the way home. Would you like to collect her now?'

Would I?! My joy knew no bounds. I was out of the house and into the car in a flash, shouting to my mother as I dashed past her. 'I'm going to get Honey! She's safe at last.'

The road flew by under the wheels and as I drove up to Mr France's house I saw his van parked by the back door. He heard me and came out to meet me. 'She's still in the back of the van,' he said, 'but be careful, she's been out for a long time and did attack my wellingtons. You don't know how she's going to react.' He, very slowly, started to open the door of the van but as soon as I saw the little, somewhat frightened face peeping at me from the dark interior of the van, I just leaned forward with the exclamation, 'Honey, where have you been?' and gathered her up into my arms. To my great delight, she covered my face with kisses, her tail wagging furiously. I just couldn't believe it. Her joy at seeing me was as great as my joy at getting her back. It was as if I had seen her only yesterday, instead of not being able to get within yards of her for nearly five months. I held her very tight in my arms whilst I thanked Mr France and chatted about his morning's work. He had been very pleased with how everything had gone. He had arrived at seven again, placed the food out and set the snare, just as he had done the previous morning. He then returned to his hidy-hole and waited. 'I had quite a pleasant time,' he said. He had enjoyed sitting quietly in the sun, admiring the view. Honey had come along, slipping quietly through the grass at about eight-thirty, after the cows had been collected. I suppose she had gone straight for her food, putting her head easily into the snare. She still had it hanging loosely round her neck as I held her. I slipped it off and returned it to its owner. He could use it again. I popped Honey into the back of my car and settled Mr France's account. I also decided to give him the reward I was offering for the recapture of Honey, so he ended up as satisfied as I was. I jumped into the car and drove home.

Although Honey was sitting quite contentedly in the back of the car, what would she be like when we were at home? She had been running wild for several months, not letting any human being within sight of her. Would she still try and vanish as she had been doing on the farm? I decided I had better keep her securely on a lead at all times and see how she reacted. We arrived home and I put a spare lead and collar on her. I always had plenty lying about in the car. I walked her into the house. She seemed quite relaxed and happy. She didn't pull or dart to try and get away as I thought she might. The little wild animal that I had expected to be bringing home seemed to be behaving like a perfectly normal pet who had perhaps been away for a couple of days. She wagged her tail and greeted my mother who had rushed out of the house when she heard the car draw up. She was delighted to say Hello to all the other dogs in the kitchen too. I then decided, as the doors were all safely closed, to let her off her lead as she seemed so relaxed and normal. She promptly went from each dog bed to the next, collected all the blankets into the one she

had always most preferred, then climbed in on top with the inevitable last blanket dripping from her mouth. She gave a huge sigh of contentment, just as if she was saying, 'Thank goodness I'm home' and relaxed!

I just could not believe my eyes. All that time away, all those hours of running and chasing, it was just as if she had been gone for a weekend and would rather be at home, thank you! Well there would certainly not be any need to keep her on the lead in the house. I was so sure she would be like a frightened fox cub when she returned, being so young when she was lost and away so long. Would she disappear under the sideboard and snap or bite if you tried to get her out? Would she have forgotten her name? It could not have been more opposite. But that was indoors, how about outside? Definitely lead and collar there. In the house I could at least catch her if she tried to run away; outside was a different matter.

We all sat down and had a celebratory cup of coffee and I decided to feed Honey as she must be pretty hungry by now. She had always been a very greedy puppy, thank goodness, and had been pretty fat when she had disappeared which definitely stood her in good stead in her fight for life. She now readily polished off her dinner, again going straight to her place in the outside kitchen where I always fed all the dogs. She seemed to have forgotten nothing. I then securely put on her lead and collar, rather tighter than usual in case she should slip it and bolt. I took her out into the garden to see what would happen in the big outside world. She trotted round perfectly happily, not a bit bothered or concerned about a thing. I just could not believe it.

The next thing to do was to get her groomed. With the long coat Beardies have, I had expected her to have a thick, solid mat all over her body. I had rescued Crofter from a bad home and it had taken me about 12 hours of hard brushing and combing to clear his coat of mats and tangles. Honey had a few small mats behind her ears and in her trousers, the rest of her coat was in perfectly groomed condition and it took me precisely half an hour to have her fully groomed. She had lost a lot of her puppy coat and the new adult coat was coming in beautifully harsh and straight over her shoulders. I also found as I groomed her that she had obviously just come into season. Whether it was the shock of being caught or the joy of coming home we shall never know but we had definitely got her back just in time.

The next thing I felt I really must do was to ring up *The Berrows* newspaper, as they had shown such interest in her story, and let them know of the happy ending. Maybe they would not be interested but then again they might. So I gave the newsdesk a call and must have just struck lucky. The lady I spoke to, who was obviously a dog lover, had remembered the story and was delighted about the outcome. Could they send a reporter and photographer and do a follow-up story? Why yes, I was only too delighted to help. Both arrived in a short space of time and I proudly showed Honey off to them. She was not so delighted and definitely would have preferred not to have her fame in the papers, poor little girl. She started to get very worried so, after they had taken a few photos, I popped her back into the kitchen and chatted on my own to the reporter. They were both very impressed by how well Honey had settled down and promised to write a nice article. I was delighted to see we had made front-page news when I bought the paper the following week. Poor Honey's little face looked very worried in her picture though.

The next thing to do was to ring up all the people who had helped so much over the last four and a half months and tell them the good news. I arranged with the cowman to take him a reward as it was definitely his contacting me that had enabled us to get her back. I also wanted to see the man who had seen Honey first from his flat in Malvern. He definitely refused any reward saying he had been only too pleased to help so I decided to take him a present of half a dozen cut-glass sherry glasses, which I hoped he could not refuse. Both he and his wife accepted them with thanks; my conscience was clear. Everyone was so delighted we had Honey back. I was on a real high. Michael came back as early as he could from the show – even that had been super. Crofter had won Best in Show and Angus had also won his class. It was one of the best days of my life.

CHAMPION

Honey had settled back into her old routine in the house so well but I was still a little concerned about the garden. Thorne Dene was a large old farmhouse surrounded by fields with a drive across a grass field up to the road. We had a large garden and orchard but it was only fenced round with hedges – something any dog could walk straight through never mind a dog so agile and capable as Honey had become in her long months of misery. I decided I would keep her on her lead at all times whenever she was outside the house, and so have some sort of control over her movements. This I did for a couple of days after she returned but, as she seemed quite happy and not in the least bit scared or bothered by any sound or experience, I thought I would risk her off the lead, just in the garden for a few moments, to see what would happen. She was fine, relaxed and happy, trotting round, not at all concerned or bothered. She visited all her favourite haunts and holes, decided everything was in the right place and she was home, happy and content.

When we went on our usual walks across the farm fields, I had kept Honey on the lead, just in case, but after a few days of her being free in the garden, decided to risk her off the lead on the walks as well.We were only going round the farm so she would not be far from home if anything should upset or spook her. We had covered most of the farm since her return home so even if she had forgotten anything, which I doubted anyway, she now had it refreshed in her memory. So on our next morning walk, I released the lead and watched her race off with all the other dogs across the field. They reached the far hedge, turned and raced back, Honey happily running with all her friends. So far, there were no problems, the whole walk was completely trouble free. Honey showed no sign of disappearing or getting worried so I felt quite confident she was perfectly all right and had suffered no ill effects from her ordeal other than the dreadful nightmares she still had regularly. All dogs dream a great deal but they usually seem to be happy dreams, paws twitching as if they are having a lovely gallop and sometimes small yaps come from the dreaming dog. I find the other dogs will look at the dreaming dog, usually give a sigh and go back to sleep themselves. Honey's dreams were different – quite definitely nightmares. I could only guess at what horrors she was reliving. She would become so distressed that I felt it was only kind to wake her up and so break the cycle of terror she was suffering again. Goodness only knows what dreadful events she had gone through during those long four and a half months. Would she ever forget those appalling experiences? I could only hope that time would dim her memory.

Beardies have excellent memories and learn very quickly, any lesson you impart to them as young puppies. Providing you maintain discipline, you will have very little trouble throughout the dog's life. As all my puppies are taught to ignore any cows, we never needed leads whilst walking on the farm. Several days had passed now, with Honey as free on her walks as all the other dogs. Now, the winter was coming on and, as December progressed, the weather was definitely deteriorating. I was so pleased that

Honey was safely home. I dreaded to think of her out on her own during the depressingly cold short days but there was no need to worry about her now, thank goodness.

Then things happened that shook my steadily mounting confidence. We were going for our usual morning walk and after a good race with the other dogs Honey was trotting along by my side. Suddenly, she dived at a stone lying in front of her. As she pounced, she looked a little disappointed sensing, perhaps, it was only a stone. I realised it looked just like an egg, lying there in the middle of the field and thought, I bet she ate lots of eggs on her travels. Then Honey seemed to falter a bit. I saw a blank look come over her eyes and she took off at a fast gallop. I shouted 'Honey! Honey!' in my most commanding voice. Luckily, she heard, understood, and stopped running, almost at the hedge. I raced over and put her safely back on her lead. The dreadful look disappeared out of her eyes, she wagged her tail and seemed to be back to her usual happy self. But I was scared. Everything seemed to have been going so well, too well in fact. I had become over confident, such a dreadful experience was not going to vanish from a puppy's mind in a few days, no matter how well she seemed to have adjusted. So back on the lead went Honey, even in the garden.

A week or so later, I decided to try her off the lead again in the garden as she had shown no signs at all of being upset since her short bolt in the field. She was fine in the garden as indeed she had been since her return home but I made up my mind to keep her on the lead on her walks for a bit longer. After a few more days, as she was so relaxed again and had not dived at any more stones in the hope they might be eggs and as she did so miss her runs with the other dogs, I felt so sorry for her that I decided I would risk letting her off the lead on her walks again. It was getting longer and longer since she had returned home and she was getting more and more settled. Even her nightmares were easing off a little. It was worth a try, I was sure. Again, for several days everything was fine. Honey would run and play with the rest of the dogs, happy and relaxed, then suddenly it happened again. Some trigger turned her mind, the terrible blank stare came into her eyes and she was off. This time I could not stop her. She seemed to have gone deaf as well. She flew across the field and into the next one. The other dogs and I raced after her and luckily Barberry caught up with her. Honey turned, seemed to collect herself and came trotting back with Barberry to be put securely on her lead.

So things progressed; she would be kept on her lead for several days. It was only on her walks, as she seemed fine in the garden: no fear, no trouble at any time. I would let her off her lead, quite safely for several days, then suddenly she would bolt. Every time she bolted, she would go a bit further and stay away a bit longer. The last time she did it was on a horrid foggy, cold morning. She vanished into the mist. I searched and called with all the dogs also doing their best to find her, but she had disappeared without trace. Well she knows her way around here I consoled myself. She can soon scent her way home. She had not been gone for more than ten minutes previously, but this time she was away for more than half an hour and that, I told myself, would definitely be the last time. If she is going to disappear like this, she will not be let off the lead again, ever. It's no good for either Honey or myself. Honey returned home, after her half-hour disappearing act, and that was the last time she ever had the opportunity to vanish throughout her life. She never tried to leave the garden but the dreadful blank look would come into her eyes at any time. It did not seem to have any obvious cause and she could be induced to lose it by very gentle stroking and talking to her. Slowly, over the years that also vanished but it took about five years before it eventually disappeared, never to return, thank goodness.

So from now on, Honey stayed securely on her lead on all the walks across the farm. The garden and orchard together were about 3 acres and she was always fine there. She had plenty of space to run and play so I did not feel cruel or that she was unduly restricted for exercise as Beardies, being working Sheepdogs, definitely need lots of free running to keep themselves happy. Honey, after nearly five months of unrestricted exercise, was a very, very fit dog. She had hard muscles all over which were never lost throughout the rest of her life. Honey was at the age that Beardies usually do a junior coat-drop after which it soon starts to grow back in. As Honey was not in a bad state, in either coat or condition, I felt why should she not resume her show career? All the other dogs of her age would also be somewhat out of coat too. She would not look out of place but how would she react to the hassle and stress of the show ring? She was definitely off men, which was hardly surprising, but rather than just put her straight into a show, I felt it would be a good idea to take her to ring craft classes, something I had never bothered with before.

When I first started dog-showing, there were no such things around but nowadays classes abounded all over the place. They were usually held in small village halls and the like. Dog show enthusiasts would gather together once a week in an evening with their puppies and dogs. It would socialise the puppies so that they got used to meeting all breeds of dogs prior to going to their first show; would be taught to behave correctly for the show ring; would be handled by a judge then walk properly at the handler's side, with Beardies on a loose lead or in the manner desired for any particular breed; and would be able to turn on a sharp corner and walk in a balanced manner in a circle. There would be a different person to act as judge each week so the dogs would accept anyone handling them. A cup of tea would be made and enjoyed by all about halfway through the evening, and it made a very pleasant night-out for both dogs and owners.

I found out where the nearest ring craft club was. They met every Tuesday evening so about a month after Honey returned, she was brushed and combed in the afternoon, popped in the car after dinner and driven to the ring craft classes. She was still pretty nervous of nearly everything outside her small world of home, not at all the happy extrovert that she had been for the first seven months of her life. She did not exactly refuse to enter the hall but certainly did not trot happily in. Once inside, and seeing all the dogs there, she soon relaxed and started to enjoy herself a bit more. She had not forgotten her show-training one jot and trotted round the small ring, doing her up-and-down with no trouble at all. It was a bit different though when the judge, who was a man, tried to go over her. She stood for a second, then decided she did not enjoy this bit and backed off fast. I decided not to force the issue. She was being basically very good and I did not want to upset her so asked for her to be excused for that night anyway. We did a couple more trots up and down and then sat for the rest of the evening just letting Honey watch everything going on around her, saying Hello to any dog who came up to her for a chat.

On the way home, I felt things had not gone too badly at all. In fact, I was quite pleased. Honey could have been really terrified, have forgotten all her pervious training or several other disasters could have happened. She could have refused to walk at all or even worse, tried to bite the judge. We would definitely go back again next week. She would soon be back in the ring at this rate. So the following Tuesday found Honey and myself in the car, off to ring craft. This time, she was much more relaxed and played

70

with some of the other young dogs. She walked up and down beautifully and even stood reasonably well for the judge who, thank goodness, was a lady this time. I went home cock-a-hoop. She was going on famously, no problems at all. We would definitely go back again the following week. So the third Tuesday we went back again. Honey seemed somewhat reluctant to go into the hall when we arrived though. She was definitely on edge as we walked in and she disappeared under my seat as I sat down to wait for the class to begin. I noticed, with regret, that it was a man-judge this time. Never mind, Honey had been so good last week, surely she would be fine as soon as the class started. We were all called into the ring and Honey came out from under my chair very reluctantly. She pulled badly on her lead instead of trotting nicely at my side, backed off from the judge so had to be held firmly to prevent her shooting backwards, and behaved as if she had never had any show-training before and had no idea of what she was supposed to be doing. The whole evening was a disaster. I went home very depressed. What on earth had got into Honey? She had been so good the previous week. We had better go again and see if she reverts back to her usual self.

So back we went the following Tuesday. Honey went into the hall, sat by my seat and trembled. She was not as bad as the previous week but was far from enjoying anything about her evening. I decided ring craft was not for Honey. It was actually doing more harm than good. I would go back to my usual method of show-training, doing all the walking triangles, and stand-and-stays on the lawn at home and just generally socialise her by taking her shopping. Honey showed me that she fully approved of this course of action by behaving to perfection in all her show-training on the lawn and trotting round the shops in a confident manner. She did not rush up to people, tail wagging, just begging to be said Hello to as she had as a puppy. She actually seemed to ignore the fact that there were people about her at all, just as a well-trained and well-behaved dog should.

So we went through the rest of the winter. Spring came bursting in with the sun getting warmer every day. The trees were growing greener by the minute. The damson trees came into blossom with the beautiful scent filling the orchard and the dog show season started up again. Why not enter Honey for a small show and see how she behaved? It was certainly worth a try. I chose one, with a lady-judge, fairly near to home so we would not have too long a car journey. The night before the show, I bathed Honey's white parts of her coat, her face, collar, shirt-fronts, legs and back paws. Her coat had come on in leaps and bounds since it had been properly looked after again, and her rich golden-brown colour was starting to develop. Her coat was a bit short for her age due to the amount she had lost on the Malvern Hills, but she still looked nice. We started off early next morning as I did not want to rush Honey into the ring. She would need time to adjust to the show atmosphere again and she also had to be groomed prior to going into the show ring.

I was glad we had gone to the few ring craft classes as Honey, although not completely relaxed, was quite all right and sat on her grooming table, seeming pretty un-perturbed. 'Please be good,' I whispered as I put her down on the floor and walked her towards the ring. As soon as she entered the ring and saw several other Beardies in it, she was transformed; her tail wagged furiously, as she pulled first to one dog then to another greeting them in pure joy. Here was my happy puppy back again. I was delighted. She had not forgotten – it was just Beardies she wanted to see at shows. She showed beautifully once more, stood well for the judge and won second in her

72

class. Everybody came over to talk to Honey and see how she was after her escapade on the Malverns. They said how fit and well she looked and how lucky I was to have her back, all of which I totally agreed with so we went home well-content with the day's proceedings.

Slowly Honey seemed to forget all her dreadful experiences. The terrible blank stare came into her eyes less and less and later, for shorter and shorter times. Her nightmares also steadily diminished, although I never let her off her lead outside the house and garden just in case she decided to bolt again.

One day, Honey had been home for about 18 months and seemed so completely settled, I decided to take her back to Malvern just to see what reaction she might have. She had been quite happy at home for some time, was back to being very friendly with everyone who came to visit, was showing and winning well. Had she forgotten her bad experience? I should have had more sense, Beardies have incredible memories. Well, we all packed into the car, several of the other dogs and Honey, just as we had been used to, and drove to Malvern. I parked in the Clock Tower Carpark just as I always used to. I opened the back of the car and, putting Honey on a strong lead and collar, let the other dogs out into the carpark, free. We all started off up the very familiar track up the hills. We soon walked past the cottage on the left, the other dogs racing ahead, really enjoying themselves as always. Honey was rather quiet. We got to the first part of the path where the hills open up in front of you. Honey suddenly shot up the steep slope on my right, pulling frantically to get away, her face a mask of terror. I pulled her back down thinking thank heavens the lead was a strong one. I then called all the dogs back and dashed down to the car. How could I be so cruel and thoughtless towards my poor puppy, putting her into such a fearful situation once more.

74

I got all the dogs back into the car and stroked and talked to Honey to calm her – she was shaking all over. I decided there and then I would never bring Honey back to Malvern again; that was definitely the last time she would ever see Malvern.

Honey was eventually able to be let off her lead for walks. When she was six years old, I moved house. Thorne Dene was sold and I bought a tiny cottage with a view of the whole range of the Malvern Hills, actually very much nearer than Thorne Dene had been to the hills. After I had been in the cottage for a couple of months and, as everything was different and Honey was now quite settled, I decided to risk her off her lead on a walk. We all knew the area well now so trusted everything would be all right. Honey was absolutely fine, showing no sign of disappearing or even giving it a thought. She behaved just like any of the other dogs. At last she had overcome her fears and had either finally forgotten her experience or gained sufficiently in confidence that she realised there was no need to bolt again. Although I never let her off the lead away from home, just in case, she never needed her lead again on her walks round the commons that surrounded my new cottage and as my orchard, this time, was securely fenced, Honey once again had complete freedom with all the other dogs. Eventually, Honey completely regained all her lost confidence. She thoroughly enjoyed all her shows and would be delighted to welcome all visitors, being extremely friendly even with men, just as she had been as a puppy. Her colour came through as a beautiful golden brown and she passed it on to her puppies.

So that is the end of Honey's story on Malvern, not quite the end of Honey's story though. She went on to become a champion and proved she was also a superb mother having some incredibly beautiful puppies, several becoming champions including Champion Willowmead Perfect

Lady, my top winning bitch, another gorgeous golden-brown Beardie, just like her mother. Lady holds the record of being the only Beardie to win the hat-trick of best bitch at Crufts for three consecutive years. In fact, every dog I have bred since Honey, goes back to Honey somewhere in the pedigree. She lived a long and happy life dying at 14½ years of age, only ever suffering from one bout of kennel cough until her terminal illness. She obviously had an extremely strong constitution to survive her ordeal with no ill effects. I will never replace Honey but see her again in all her descendants, going on through the generations. Her type and happy temperament are still all around me and I hope will live on forever.

HONEY'S STORY

1

Honey had always loved the trips to the Malvern Hills. She would race ahead of the other dogs, never too far, always looking back over her shoulder to make sure someone was just behind and that everyone was in sight. The fateful day in early June when disaster struck started with no portent of the terrible mishap that would happen before the day was out. The dogs always travelled well and sat waiting as good as gold as the car turned into the Clock Tower Carpark. The car was parked in the shade as this was going to be a very quick walk, only half an hour, and Grandmother was going to sit in the car and wait.

All the dogs leapt out when the back of the estate was lifted and the command to get out was issued. They knew the way without being told, straight up the path, never towards the road, going past the only cottage on the left. Shortly after passing the cottage they would always go up one of the very narrow little paths leaving the wide main path to wind slowly round the hill to the top. The small path went straight up the steep slope, joining the main path directly above. You could walk around North Hill along the main path and go for either a quick walk or a long one, as the mood or time allowed.

As it's always quicker going downhill and home,

everyone went for 20 minutes up North Hill then Suzanne decided that would be far enough, time to turn for home. All the dogs were called to 'about turn' and started retracing their steps. The dogs at once started to race ahead on the way home. They soon steadied up and were trotting along happily. It was very rare to meet any other people walking over North Hill mid-afternoon as most people would either stay on the lower paths or go straight for the Beacon. But this afternoon an elderly gentleman was also out walking. He was coming towards the dogs, striding along at a good pace, with a walking-stick swinging in his hand. Honey as usual was out in front and Honey loved people. A nice man – he would be sure to be pleased to see her, so she trotted happily towards him to say Hello. But to her dismay all she got was a whack from the stick in reply to her wagging tail and smiling face.

The man also made a very strange noise, something between a grunt and a snarl. Honey was shocked and hurt. She had never had anything of this nature done to her before so she jumped back. The man still came on towards her, waving his stick in a threatening manner. Honey's courage failed her. She turned and ran as fast as her legs would carry her, not seeing or looking for anything – the other dogs, Suzanne, nothing. She ran round the bend of the hill and realised she could no longer see the man but, through her fear, suddenly heard her name being called. 'Honey. Honey.'

She stopped running and listened, realising she could no longer see any of the other dogs. There it was again, her name being called. 'Honey. Honey.'

I must get back, she thought and ran back a few steps along the path the way she had come, towards the ridge of the hill. She looked round the bend and, horror of horrors, suddenly saw, almost upon her, the dreadful man waving

his stick at her in the most frightening manner and making that dreadful noise.

Honey, who had never been hit in her life and was terribly shocked by it, didn't stop to see Suzanne and all the other dogs beginning to run towards her as they were some way back along the path, behind the man. Sheer terror took hold and Honey just fled as fast as her legs would carry her, straight along the path. Her only thought was to put as much distance between herself and this demon with the stick as she could, and as running was the best way to achieve this, Honey was going to run. But no dog can run forever. As her fear abated and her breath was getting short, she started to slow down. She was beginning to drop to a trot from a blind-panic bolt, when she suddenly saw another crowd of people appear in front of her, along the path. It was a large crowd with several children running and playing. Fear suddenly took hold of Honey again. She couldn't go back, the man was behind her. She couldn't go forward – more people, maybe more sticks! She fled uphill into the deep bracken, running fast again. She wove, turned and twisted through the bracken, up hill and down again. Several times she tried to slow down but suddenly fear would return and she felt she had to go on again. But no seven-month-old puppy can run on indefinitely and eventually she dropped into a small dip behind a rocky outcrop and lay there exhausted. The hills seemed to have become very quiet. She could no longer hear any human voices and eventually she fell into a restless sleep.

When she awoke, feeling calmer, she realised she also felt very hungry. Dinner-time was usually between four and five o'clock. As it was starting to get dark, it was nearer ten o'clock. Even worse than being hungry, Honey was extremely thirsty. All that running had built up both thirst and appetite to far more than even a basically healthy puppy would feel. It was definitely time to go home, but where was home? In fact, where on earth was she? Poor Honey had no idea which way to even start to travel. She had run so far and fast, twisting and turning so many times. She did not have the slightest idea which way to start to go to find the carpark and hopefully the car, to jump in and be driven home to a good long drink and a much-needed dinner.

Honey climbed out of her little nest and up onto the rocky outcrop to look around and survey the area that she found herself in. Nothing looked at all familiar. Nothing smelled familiar either. She was sure she had never been on this part of the hills before. Honey lifted up her head and sniffed the air. No, there didn't seem to be any familiar scents around at all. Should she go uphill again, or down? Perhaps down would be best, the carpark was usually down. So she decided to try and find a path and hopefully her lost family. As the Malverns are covered with paths it didn't take long to find one and Honey trotted along it. Suddenly she had a strange scent come on the breeze, a good scent, an animal scent. She crept slowly forward and saw, grazing peacefully, about a dozen sheep. As she was upwind from them she had scented them first, but the sheep didn't take long to realise something was there. All heads came up and stared towards the nervous puppy but very soon realised she did not constitute a threat so went back to grazing. Honey felt comforted by the sight of the sheep and not nearly so alone. She stayed by them for a few minutes then her thirst made its presence felt, more strongly than before. She really must find water soon so she tiptoed round the sheep, who completely ignored her now, and continued along the path.

As luck would have it, although Honey had galloped for several miles, she had been going up and down and round in circles rather than in a straight line. So she actually was not very far from where she had started out in her mad gallop. As she trotted along, not really having any idea of which way to go, she sniffed the ground. Suddenly it smelled familiar. It was Juno's scent, then the scent of all the other dogs and Suzanne's as well. Honey's tail wagged vigorously. Her head was down sniffing here, there and everywhere. This was better. She started to travel along the path, her nose telling her exactly which way to go. She recognised the path now too, it was the usual path down to the carpark. Everything was going to be all right at last. It did not take her long to arrive at the carpark but, horror! there was no car there at all, not her own car nor any other car either. She could smell the place where it had stood and all the scents of the other dogs where they had jumped into the car. Slowing, she tracked the tyres to the road but there she had to stop. Too many other cars had driven along the road by now and obliterated the scents of Suzanne's car tyres.

She sat at the side of the road in despair. What on earth should she do now? Then she heard the noise of a car approaching along the road and saw the lights coming towards her at speed. It seemed to rush right at her and Honey shot backwards, turned and fled back up the hills in renewed terror. She had never been out at night before and certainly not seen a car with headlights coming straight at her. She had only travelled in the car in daylight so did not know anything about headlights. The hills were quiet and dark. She would be better and safer in the bracken with the sheep for company.

But this did not give her either food or water and she really needed both. She quickly recovered her equilibrium and relaxed down to a trot. Natural instincts started to reassert themselves. Her head came up and she sniffed the air for water. Nothing came into her nostrils but she continued along the lower path that she had found herself on. Once again, her head came up and she sniffed hard.

Surely that scent was water and – glory be! food too. She was actually approaching the café at Saint Anne's Well. The café was a somewhat run-down affair, at the time Honey was lost, but the well was still there and so were litter bins, and litter bins contained all sorts of food-scraps.

The area smelled strongly of humans – unknown humans. Would these also have large sticks and hard voices. Honey slowed down to a walk, stopping at the entrance to the café forecourt. She looked around most carefully and scented hard, her nose twitched and her eyes scanned the whole area. She was ready to jump back in a flash and race away again should something dreadful reappear. But no, all was quiet and peaceful, no sound or sight of anything but a small mouse who had come out after the food-scraps as well. Honey saw the mouse and remembered the one she had caught in the moat bank when she had been five months hold. She forgot her fear for an instant and rushed forward to pounce on the mouse. This time she was not quick enough and the mouse scuttled away into a crevice of rock. But it had given Honey her courage back for a minute and she thought, if a mouse is all right here, maybe I will be too. And now, thirst and hunger were outweighing her fears. Honey walked towards the drinking-fountain. It stood about human-waist height. She stood up on her hind legs and could just reach into the water with her tongue. My word, that water tasted good.

When she had drank her fill, food was the next thought. She was beginning to regain some of her confidence and sniffed along the ground for crumbs and bits of food dropped by the visitors of the previous day, not a lot for a hungry puppy! She could smell food in the litter bins and as she had stood up on her hind legs to get at the water, she stood up on the edge of the litter bin to see if she could get the food – of course it fell over with a terrible clatter of

85

metal landing on concrete. Honey shot back in terror. What had she done? Always having a strong sense of what was right and what was wrong, she knew that knocking bins over was wrong and it sounded much louder in the quiet of the night. Honey nearly fled again but, as all was instantly still and nobody appeared to reprove her for her misdeeds, after an initial leap back and a turn to flee, she pulled herself together realising the smell of food was more distinct than before the top had fallen off the litter bin. Out had tumbled several old sandwiches and bits of crust. Half-eaten cakes lay strewn in front of her amongst tin cans of coke, pop bottles and other general rubbish from the litter bin.

Honey rapidly stepped forward again and began to polish off everything that was the least bit edible. Although it really was not a very satisfactory meal, it did fill in a little hole and her hunger was certainly not nearly so acute. She decided to have a good sniff at the next litter bin and see if there was any food in that one too. She tried her trick of standing up against the bin and again it fell over with the same clatter. Honey leapt back as before but was far more confident this time. There were the same food-scraps and she made a rapid meal of all edibles. There were three bins on the café patio; Honey polished off all the food from the three bins. She then decided to have another drink from the water-fountain to complete her meal.

Now to go home! She was beginning to get a little fed up with the lonely life on the hills. She was used to being in a crowd of dogs and people. She decided she was definitely missing the company. Honey again retraced her steps to where she had found the scent of her family going back to the carpark but she hesitated to go into the carpark in case the monster with the brilliant lights should come rushing at her again. Honey sat for a couple of hours, looking and watching towards the carpark. Surely someone should have come and fetched her by now. Slowly it started to get light. Nights in mid-June are relatively short. Honey yawned, she really had missed her night's sleep. She had better go and find somewhere safe to have a doze. She wandered back up the hill and mooched around. It didn't take long to find a nice warm nest hidden well in the high bracken and a very tired little dog curled up and fell fast asleep.

2

Honey woke with start. She could hear voices fairly near to her. She hadn't realised, when she fell asleep, that she was near to a path, and a couple were out for an early walk. Honey stayed dead still. These were not voices that she knew; maybe they also had big sticks. She peeped out from the bracken and saw the people striding along. Again, the man had a walking-stick which he swung vigorously as he walked. Honey started to shake. Fear was building up in her to an unreasonable degree and, with no one to soothe that fear it was starting to take her over again. She quietly turned and slipped away using the bracken as cover.

She carried on for quite a bit and then, to her relief, scented the sheep again. Those were nice, they were also company. As the sheep scented Honey all their heads came up but they didn't panic. They just stood watching her, their jaws chewing rhythmically as Honey dropped to a down position on her tummy, and stayed quite quiet. The sheep soon lost interest in her, continuing to graze steadily. The sheep moved off the small enclosure that Honey had found them on and wandered along ending up on one of the paths. The day, which was fine again, also brought out the people to walk the hills. Honey, who had steadily followed the sheep, creeping along behind them, heard voices again. Honey froze as she saw a huge dog, completely out of control, rushing towards the sheep who disappeared at a gallop down the path. Honey bolted into the bracken and fled. The owners of the dog soon called him back so no harm was done except Honey had lost her friends. She was also beginning to get really hungry and thirsty again as she was used to being fed twice a day. It was definitely breakfast-time by now. She heard too many people around now though, so she lay up in the bracken and decided to sleep the day away.

Round about six o'clock the hills became quiet again as nearly everyone had returned home for their dinner or tea and once again Honey was extremely hungry and even more thirsty. She remembered the way to Saint Anne's Well so purposefully trotted off in that direction. She reached the café without meeting any more people or having any mishaps. The café closed at six o'clock. Luckily, Honey didn't arrive until six-thirty so it was all peaceful and quiet. It didn't look so spooky and frightening as it had in the middle of the night so Honey went straight to the drinking-fountain and had a good long drink. When her thirst slackened she turned her attention to the litter bins again. It was a matter of seconds to tip up the first one and root around in the contents for all the food scraps and soon all three bins had been upended and all the food devoured. It really wasn't very much, nothing like as appetising and satisfying as her own food at home, but it was certainly better than nothing and at least it was food.

She then began to roam the hills. She felt much safer when she could no longer hear human voices at every turn. She was quietly trotting along through the bracken when suddenly a bird flew up, almost from under her nose. She stopped dead. Was it something to be afraid of again? She busily scented the air, walked forward a couple of steps and almost trod straight into the nest the sitting bird had

been trying to hide from her. Honey's head went straight down. Eggs! Lovely eggs! She knew the smell of eggs from her raids into the stockyard after hens' eggs with her mother, and eggs were much nicer than the old bits of sandwich which had been her mainstay for two days now. It was a matter of seconds to polish of all four eggs and Honey felt considerably better for it. She thought to herself, so eggs can be just lying on the ground, can they? She would keep a very sharp eye open for any signs of nest or eggs from now onwards.

She slowly ranged over the hills, getting to know her area – all of North Hill and going over towards the Beacon. As night came on, and as she had only dozed very fitfully throughout the day continually listening for voices, she decided she had better find a decent nest. It didn't take long. She soon found an overhang of rock with a thick bed of bracken to lie on and high bracken growing all around so nobody could possibly see her. She was nowhere near any path so hopefully no human would even start to come towards her hidy-hole and disturb her rest. She crept into it and fell into a deep sleep which was only disturbed by dreadful nightmares of men with sticks and cars rushing towards her, headlights shining into her eyes.

She woke up early next morning feeling hungry and thirsty again. More hungry by now. She had an ample water supply but food was another matter. A seven-month old Beardie is still growing fast and needs plenty of good nourishing food to maintain her growth. Honey had only had a few scraps and found small eggs for two days – not nearly enough. She trotted along the increasingly familiar path to Saint Anne's Well, had a nice long drink from the water-fountain and looked at the litter bins. They were all tipped up exactly as she had left them the night before with no food left in them at all. This was a blow. Honey wandered disconsolately from bin to bin, ferreting about through the rubbish for maybe a scrap she might have missed, but she had always been a good tidy-upper and not a crumb was to be found. Slowly she wandered off. She started to trot along the path. She had better see if she could find some more eggs as there was no food in the bins.

She was beginning to realise humans did not visit the hills either early morning or late evening so she felt reasonably confident going along the paths. She was still keeping mainly to North Hill but travelling slowly further and further around the area, going more up the Beacon but keeping well away from the roads. She was going along a lower path when suddenly her nose twitched. This was a new smell, something familiar. Sheep but not the right smell for the sheep she had been keeping company with. This was different. She drew nearer and the smell became overpowering. Then she saw it. One very dead sheep lying just off the path. Instinct took over, dead sheep was meat and meat was food even though she had never been fed raw meat. As with nearly all dogs these days, she had been fed a prepared, cooked dog food but the wild carnivore is only just under the surface of any dog and Honey was no exception. Also she was getting very hungry. This was a feast indeed.She saw where the crows, always the first on any carcase, had already started their work so she decided it would do very well to join them.She tucked in and ate her fill. Time slipped by and a somewhat more replete Honey decided it was time to retreat to her nest for the rest of the day whilst the people were about on the hills.

Honey slept better that day than the previous day. She was already beginning to adapt to her new style of life, sleeping most of the day away, coming out to forage for food early morning and evening-time. Her habit of sleeping throughout the night, which she had done for the first seven months of her life, was still with her and so she slept for most of the dark hours. The dead sheep lasted her for several days getting more and more ripe as the heat of mid-summer and the work of the flies, which abound in the bracken, were doing their job. One evening though, when Honey went to have another meal of lamb – somewhat ripe by now, she discovered it had gone, disappeared completely. There were smells aplenty of human feet all round where the corpse had lain – one of the rangers had spotted the sheep carcase on his regular trip round the hills checking paths to be repaired and which areas of bracken and brambles would need cutting back to keep the hills in good order. He had soon smelled the by now rotting carcase and removed it for disposal.

Poor Honey! She was now back to raiding litter bins and finding eggs again. As she had increased her boundaries she had discovered there was another café on top of the Beacon so she also raided those bins but during the week there was not a great deal to be had even from both cafés, and eggs did not reappear in the nests she raided. Wild birds are not like chickens who go back and lay in the same nest every day, they go off and and find a better, safer home to lay their eggs in so that was not too good a source of food.

Honey was by now over her main fears and was learning to slip away quietly at a gentle trot rather than a mad gallop if she saw something she was not sure of or considered could be frightening. The sheep were so used to her being with them so regularly that they never even lifted their heads as she would slip quietly through the flock. She would use the flock as a shield from anything such as a human being that frightened her, always keeping a sheep's body between herself and the strange or upsetting thing so you could hardly even see the little brown shadow slipping quietly away.

One day, about ten days after she had been lost, she was

going along on her usual trip towards Saint Anne's Well for her drink. It was about six-thirty in the evening, usually a very quiet time on the hills. Over the top of the hill she came trotting quietly down the bank and then along the path on her regular way when she suddenly stopped dead. There were people on the path. Horror! It was usually so quiet at this time. She just turned and disappeared back into the bracken and away. If only she had known it was Suzanne who had come to try to find her, but Honey was by now so wild she would not get near enough to anyone for a call to reach her and thus regain that confidence and be taken home again. Honey left the path towards Saint Anne's Well and dropped down to a much lower path, had her drink at the well and went off on her usual search for food. Much later, that evening, she was going back to her nest along the usual path that she had left so hurriedly earlier, when she suddenly stopped and sniffed the air. All the time she was out these days, to stay alive and well, it was imperative to be able to read the different scents that were borne in to her on the wind. This scent was good, it smelt just like her dinner from home. She dropped off the path into the bracken, her nose twitching vigorously, straight to the little clearing under the small windswept trees. Halfway down the slope, there it was, a whole pile of her favourite dinner just sitting there waiting to be eaten. There was also a strong smell of Suzanne and Barberry that was marvellous. She felt so much happier to have those familiar scents all round her. She sat on the spot for a couple of hours. If only they were here. Maybe they would come back for her but a group of late-evening hikers were coming along the path, laughing and chatting, so Honey reluctantly slipped away to her nest for the night.

The next morning it was pouring with rain. The lovely long dry spell had broken. Honey, having had a good meal the night before and never liking getting wet, stayed warm and dry in her little nest all day. By late evening, the rain eased off a bit and she decided it was time to go out foraging again. She trotted off as usual to Saint Anne's Well for her drink then decided to go back to the spot where she had found her food the previous night. Joy of joys, there it was again, a good portion of dinner which was rapidly devoured. Life was definitely looking up. She mooched about, going further and further over the range of hills. She had already gone well-past the Beacon now and had almost reached British Camp, the furthest point of the Malvern Hills range. Life was getting pretty much into a routine and looked as if it would continue so.

Then the whole even tenor erupted with a bang. It was mid-summer and there was always a summer party held on the Beacon on mid-summer's night. Dozens of people climb the hills at midnight and have a fine old time usually having brilliant lights with them that can be seen for miles. Honey, who was out on her evening stroll, suddenly almost ran into a huge crowd streaming up the hill. She was on the wrong side of the people to her nest so had to flee away from North Hill and towards British Camp. She only just avoided another large crowd coming towards her from the other side of the hills so flew up the hill to get away but there were even more people in that direction. She had never seen so many people on the hills and all so noisy! They were out for a good time and a party. She began to bolt again, all her new-found courage deserting her. She just ran, over a road, no traffic on it thank goodness, and over some strange hard metal things that hurt her toes and stretched away long and straight into the distance for what seemed miles, it actually was the railway lines, but Honey had never seen either a train or a railway track before.

She eventually slowed and calmed down. She trotted along, goodness only knows where she was again. But suddenly she smelt a smell from home. Cows! Although the farm she had been brought up on did not have any sheep, there had been plenty of cows all around her home. She had regularly gone for walks through the fields with cows everywhere. They would stand by the gate and loved to wallow in the pool just to one side of the gate and were easy-going, friendly things. Honey sniffed appreciatively and trotted towards the cows. These cows, although they were Friesians just like the cows at home, were different. They were not used to seeing a dog let alone a Beardie. They reacted quite differently. They all bunched up together and blew hard down their nostrils. Honey stopped dead and tried to look friendly. She was not sure what she had done wrong; no cow had disliked her before. Luckily, the cows soon sensed she was not some mad marauding dog about to chase them, and started to relax. Honey sat down at the side of the field and thought she had better take stock of her situation.

3

As Honey remained still and quiet, the cows strolled over to her to investigate this unusual little dog. They came as a bunch, very cautiously to start with but growing steadily bolder. They all stopped dead a couple of feet away, lowered their heads and blew hard down their nostrils. Honey sat her ground. Cows had never been aggressive to her in the past, her mother had often sat for ages keeping the cows in the pool round the gate at home. They were nothing to worry about; the company was nice so she slowly wagged her tail at them as a sign of friendship. Somehow the cows seemed to realise all was well. This was nothing to be afraid of, quite the opposite in fact. It was something to ignore rather than anything to give them a fright. The first one turned away and started to go back to grazing and, within a couple of minutes, the rest of the herd had followed suit.

Honey sat in her spot for some time. It was lovely and quiet in the field but it was a beautiful night and this could not be the same all the time. Rain would come again and Honey hated rain and getting wet. Should she go back to her nest on Malvern or should she stay where she was and see if it was possible to find a new nest? She decided to look around her new area and find out the prospects of staying there. Dawn comes very early in June and July so she didn't have very long in the darkness in which to look about. She followed the tracks the cows had made from being taken twice a day for milking and soon ended up in the farmyard. Slowly she sniffed about. The smell of humans was everywhere but she had learnt that smell was nothing to be afraid of. As long as you could not see anybody about you were usually safe. There were several sheds with nice warm, dry hay bales in and straw under the Dutch barn just like at home. She really began to feel she might be safer here, it was so much like home.

She started to trot around looking for eggs. The Dutch barn was always where the eggs were at home but the chickens were not free range on this farm as they had been at home so she did not have the satisfaction of an egg supper. Poor Honey was beginning to feel very tired. She had usually had a good few hours' sleep in her nest by now but had been up all night, so far. She made her way back to the cows' field and found them all lying asleep, gently chewing the cud. Honey decided she would follow suit and found a nice little indentation under a thick bit of hedge, curled up and went to sleep.

She now slept very lightly and awoke with a sense of dread. She could smell a human coming. She lay quite still and peeped out through the branches of the hedge. The field gate was opened and a cheery voice called up the cows who had started to stroll down towards the gateway and disappeared for milking. Poor Honey thought her new friends had deserted her but as the man had not even tried to come into the field, just stood at the gate and called the cows and had left following the last straggler, leaving the gate open, Honey decided to stay where she was, safely hidden for a bit, and see what would happen next. She didn't have long to wait either. Suddenly all the cows re-appeared, walking back in through the open gate and fanned out all over the field, steadily munching at the grass. The cowman slapped the last one on her rump as she went through the gate and with a cheery 'There you are girls, see you all tonight', closed the gate and, whistling happily, went on his way back to the farm for breakfast.

Honey also, gave some thought to breakfast. She had not had any bits from the café litter bins and was beginning to feel distinctly peckish. It was time to go and do her morning forage for food. She trotted steadily along, exploring her new territory. It wasn't long before she came to a road but it was a small country lane without much traffic. Honey stopped and listened for any cars but it was all silent so she trotted across and explored further. She found a nest of birds' eggs once again, so had a quick breakfast, much to the anger of the small bird whose family it was going to be. Honey spent the day exploring her new-found terrain. It was all so much quieter than the hills. She decided to make it home and remain; she just had to find a new nest. She carried on, round and round, never going too far from the field with the cows in. They were definitely her friends and companions. She needed company and had no intention of losing the cows again.

There was a small orchard of old trees near to the cows' field. It was all a bit neglected with long uncut grass round the trees and the bracken from the Malverns was starting to get established in one corner. Honey crept under the bracken and into a small nest just by the hedge. It was cool here, very quiet and peaceful – no sound of the farm workers and near to her cows. She decided this would do for the time being. As she had travelled round the farm she had found something she had not encountered on the Malverns but knew all about from home, and that was barbed wire. Her lovely long puppy-coat soon started to get pulled out on the barbs as she slipped under, over or through the strands that were in most of the hedges which divided the fields into different sections. Another advantage of being on the farm was, in several fields, there was a nice water trough for the cattle, just like at home. So, there was no problem with having to find water, it was all over the place.

Two days passed with Honey on the farm. She steadily travelled over the area going onto the neighbouring farms too. Slowly she regained her confidence, but kept well away from humans. There was no way she was going to let any human anywhere near her again. She was also getting increasingly hungry. She remembered the proper dogs' dinner she had started to find on the spot just above Saint Anne's Well. She decided she would have to go back there and see if it was still arriving each day, as she had become accustomed to just before her dreadful fright. Somehow she had to retrace the footsteps of her flight and go back to the hills. She had become very good at scenting her way around and that night she started back.

She came back to the railway lines and crossed them. Luckily, again, there wasn't a train coming, so no danger there. She next came to the main road. She slowed down as she approached it. She could hear quite a lot of traffic travelling back and forth. She had got over her fright of the first car she had seen on her first night alone on the hills, hunger was really pushing her so she sat and waited at the side of the road for some time until all was quiet, and then trotted across. She rejoined the hills at the British Camp end and purposely made her way along the bottom path towards North Hill. Halfway along, she struck off uphill and travelled past the Beacon and over the top of North Hill, always keeping off the paths. She then travelled downhill, through the sheep, who had certainly not forgotten her scarcely lifting their heads as she slipped through the flock, to where her food used to be. Joy of joys, there it was all nicely put out, a good dinner. There was also a strong smell of magpies and lots of their droppings in the area. They had found her food on the days she had not been for it and decided they also liked dog food and had eaten quite a bit of it but it had been replaced each day very late in the evening. The birds, therefore, had not had time to get to it the night Honey returned, so she had a good meal.

There was another scent there though, something was different. She looked around then saw it, something large and metal, all hidden with bracken. She sniffed and looked around. There was a large juicy bone lying inside a cage, just tempting a little dog to step inside and have a good chew but the cage smelt of fear. Honey backed away – no bone was going to tempt her inside. Honey had finished her dinner and felt replete. It was a good meal but she might just as well check out the litter bins whilst she was here and have a quick drink. So a visit was made to Saint Anne's Well. As it was about two in the morning it was all quiet and peaceful. Now for the trip back to the farm before the day broke and people started to climb the hills again. She negotiated both the road and the railway with no trouble and arrived back at her nest to sleep away what remained of the night.

So her new routine began. She liked to get up fairly early and would go and see the cows every morning at around seven. She would watch them being taken off to be milked and usually stayed to see them back into the field. Then she would mooch around the farm, looking for bits and bobs that might be edible, throughout the rest of the morning. She slept most of the afternoon throughout the heat of mid-summer and then strolled around during the evening, finally making her trip to the hills, either in the evening or crack of dawn, for her food. Then came the terrible evening when she saw her first train, just before she crossed the railway lines. She was trotting along – she rarely went any faster than a steady trot these days, just like a fox who never seems to break that steady effortless ground-covering trot. As she approached the railway lines she heard a noise like thunder in the distance. She stopped dead and listened. It rapidly became louder and the ground started to vibrate. Honey stood petrified, then saw this monster rushing towards her along the hard metal strips. In an instant it had raced past her and gone. Honey shook from head to toe but it had disappeared. She had learnt that once a thing had gone, it was now safe so very slowly she went on over the tracks and along her way. So long as you waited at the roadside for cars to pass, and now kept a wary eye open for trains and waited for them to pass, you had nothing to worry about, it seemed.

She continued to go her way up to the hills and eat her food which was replaced every day as regular as clock-work. It was not always the same amount; sometimes the magpies had found it first but they never ate the lot so there was always something for Honey. It did seem strange though, it was never quite in the same place. It would be about 3 or 4 inches along towards the cage every night. Then one day, it was actually right up to the cage door. The bone was changed every so often but it was always inside the cage and no way was Honey going to put a foot inside. The night she found the food actually at the cage door she panicked. The smell of fear was too strong. She just could not touch it, her fear far outweighing her hunger. She left the area without even a mouthful and went back to the farm very disconsolately. She would just have to be hungry for a while again. She travelled back again the next night and, joy of joys, there was her food about 6 feet away from the dreaded cage so it was quite safe. She polished the lot off with relish.

Slowly the days slipped into weeks. One night she did her usual trip and arrived at dawn for her breakfast, rather than dinner these days. The fog had come down just as it usually did now. There wasn't any dog meat laid out for her as usual, instead there were some nice crunchy biscuits which she quickly polished off. She had always liked her biscuits at home before she got lost. She wandered off after finishing the biscuits and started to make her way back to the farm. She was halfway over the hills when she started to feel extremely weird. Her legs did not seem to want to go where she wanted them to and she suddenly started to feel very tired. She must find somewhere to sleep in safety – and quickly. She remembered her first nest and struggled to retrace her steps back to North Hill and find it. She just made it before her legs gave out completely. She fell into a deep, deep drugged sleep. She certainly had a good long sleep and woke up quite a few hours later, luckily none the worse for her sedation.

As she was still on the hills, she made her way back to her food spot. Luckily, the usual food was there again. After she had eaten it, she certainly felt a great deal better. The food absorbed a lot of the sedation pills and, although still feeling somewhat drowsy, she was now rather thirsty so Honey trotted along to Saint Anne's Well to have a good long drink. She did her usual clean up of the bins then decided she would go back home to the farm. She was missing the company of the cows. She quietly slipped up the hills, over the top past the Beacon and soon found herself back in the field with her cows. They scarcely even lifted up their heads as she trotted along the hedgerow, just like the sheep on the hills. The sedation was still in her system so Honey decided it would be a good idea to have another long sleep and so crept into her nest in the bracken and dozed for a few more hours.

Honey continued her daily routine of travelling for her food. It would be left out each day and steadily moved a few inches towards the cage but as soon as it was at the cage door she panicked and left it strictly alone. Then it would be moved back to about 6 feet away and so the slow movement back to the cage would start, until the food reached the cage door to be left untouched once more.

4

Because the magpies were also eating quite a bit of Honey's food, especially when it was put out earlier in the evening, she was not getting sufficient rations. She was having a great deal of exercise and had lost all her puppy-fat in the first few days of near starvation. She remained in a state of constant hunger. The eggs she found, never too plentiful, rapidly became less and less as the summer progressed so her main preoccupation was looking for food. With the water troughs on the farm, her water supply was plentiful.

One morning, the wind had shifted to a new direction when Honey woke up. She lifted her head and sniffed hard. Surely that was a new scent, not too good for a human nose but very interesting to a dog who is really a scavenger. The new smell was from the local tip, the day before had been dustbin day and there were some very rich smells wafting along on the breeze. Honey, with her head held high, began to follow the scents. The tip was quite a distance across the fields but it didn't take too long to reach it. Lots of birds were there already, picking over the refuse for any edible bits and Honey soon joined them. Humans are incredibly wasteful beings so there was quite a good supply of relatively edible scraps. That was the first of many trips Honey made to the tip and the extra food she managed to scavenge, along with the food from the hills, really kept her in excellent condition.

Life was not quite so bad these days. She had the company of the cows and sufficient food and water. She saw very few people as she avoided humans as much as possible and, whilst the weather was not too bad, her bracken nest was warm and dry. But English summers do not stay warm and dry for very long and this, although a pretty fair summer, was no exception turning wet and much colder for a spell. The rain dripped and dripped continuously for two days. Poor Honey's bracken bed became a sodden mess and, although Honey curled herself into a tighter and tighter ball, she soon became a soggy little dog. When the rain finally stopped, the sun once again shone forth rapidly drying up the trees and bracken plus a somewhat damp and dishevelled brown Beardie. Honey decided she must find a dryer and warmer nest. She did not want to leave the cows too far away so busied herself by exploring in far more detail her surroundings.

She dare not go into the barns and outbuildings during the day, there were far too many people around, so it would have to be out in the fields somewhere. She really liked the old orchard best of all, no one ever came into it so she felt secure and comfortable there. It was next to the cows' field so she did not feel lonely. She wandered round the hedgerows wondering if she could find somewhere there. Lying across her path was a big pear tree. It had been brought down by some very bad gales a couple of years before, during the winter. The grass had grown up and almost over the big strong trunk of the tree so almost hiding it from view. Honey hopped up and sat on top of the wide trunk and looked around from her vantage point. Slowly she looked at the ground below her, then hopped down. At the base of the tree, where the roots were still half in the ground, was a beautiful little hole. The trunk was above, to keep out rain and wind, the roots covered one side and, at the moment, the long thick grass made a complete shield round all sides. This was perfect. The ground was bone dry and the mouse that had been living there previously, rapidly vacated her nest as Honey moved in . . .

Honey dug vigorously to make her new home into a nice cosy little hole, just like the big hole that she had helped all the other Beardie girls dig under the box bush at home. She soon had it deep and cosy. The walls would also shelter her and keep her both cool in summer and warm in winter. This was perfect and Honey, after her exertions, curled up and went to sleep prior to her trip to the hills in the early hours of the morning for her food.

Honey had now developed the habit of sitting in the cows' field. After her first breakfast from the hills, she would scavenge her second from the tip on her way home. She would, on her return home, have a good drink first then sit and contemplate the world from the top of the bank at the far end of the field, away from the farm gate. The first few times Honey had smelled the cowman coming towards the field, she had vanished like a wraith. But as he just stood at the gate and called the cows down to him for milking, Honey soon lost her fear that he would hurt her or try to catch her. Slowly she left later and later and eventually held her ground and remained sitting there watching him come and go with interest.

Then a momentous event occurred. She was trotting along the hedge one evening, fairly late, to the water trough for a drink when suddenly her nose twitched and a very familiar scent came to her. Her food! She quickened her pace and there it was, just under the wire, in one of her favourite places for popping through from one field to another. What joy! She polished it off with delight. A really good meal tonight – the magpies had not found it

yet so she had a full meal. She felt really replete but in the early hours of the morning she still made the trip to her other meal place on the hills. She was not too pleased though as, for the first time, she found no food there at all. She mooched about disconsolately for a bit, looking all round in case it had moved to a new place. The dreaded cage was still there with the tempting bone still inside but she was really rather full so it certainly did not induce her to even give it a second glance, never mind think about getting it out of the cage. She had a wander round the hills, said Hello to the sheep then trotted off home to the farm and her cows.

The next evening Honey thought she would just check the spot where she had found her food the night before and, to her delight there it was again in exactly the same spot. So once more a good meal was had. She still went up on the hills overnight to do a double check on her old food spot but after a few trips of finding nothing left there, and always food near the water trough on the farm, she started not to bother going up on the hills regularly. Instead, she spent all her time on the farm with regular trips to the tip to forage.

One day, shortly after the day she started to find her food on the farm, she was trotting along the top of the orchard to go to her nest after a trip to the tip, when she saw strange people walking along the bottom of the orchard just coming in from the cows' field. Honey very rapidly slipped away using the long grass as cover. She vanished quickly and silently through the hedge and disappeared from view. She travelled over several fields and dropped into another nest she knew of and stayed there for several hours, very quiet and still. As the evening wore on, she could not hear a sound, so she peeped out and sniffed the air. There was nothing untoward, as far as she could ascertain. So she decided to go and see if her dinner had arrived. It was now somewhat later than her usual meal-time and she was definitely rather peckish. As she entered the orchard on the way to the cows' field and dinner, she suddenly stopped and sniffed hard at the ground. Surely that scent was Angus, one of her old Beardie companions from home. His scent was all over the orchard. There were strong scents of Suzanne and several of the other dogs too. Slowly Honey, her nose glued to the ground and tail gently wagging, went all over the orchard taking in those lovely longed-for scents. She suddenly felt terribly homesick as she remembered her old life, a life of peace, comfort and happiness with no dreadful frights and terrors at every turn. Not as her life was at the moment, never knowing where her next meal would come from with any certainty or if some dreadful train or human would terrify her again.

But the only thing she had was a faint scent with no nice humans to take her home so, with her tail and ears droop-ing, sadly she wandered into the field with her cow friends and made her way to her dinner. Even that was not very large tonight. It had been put out somewhat earlier in the day so the magpies had found it first and thrown it around eating quite a bit too. So poor Honey did not even get a decent meal that night either. She ate every scrap she could find and sadly trotted back to her nest under the fallen tree for the night.

Slowly the scents of her family faded and her life went back to its even keel of a few days before and so it con-tinued for a few more weeks.

One Saturday, Honey was quietly trotting along for her evening meal as usual. Yes, there it was, in the same place as always. She polished it off in her usual fast way. You didn't mess around with your eating if you might have to bolt for safety at any second. Just as she was finishing it she thought she detected a rather nasty taste but had swal-lowed it too fast to really notice. She mooched about for a bit then suddenly stiffened. She caught the scent of several strangers. She stood stock still and then saw them. Two men trying to hide just a short way away. She turned quickly and trotted off. They steadily got up from their hiding place and followed her. Honey quickened her pace. She did not have time to go down the hedge to her usual hole so jumped over the five-barred gate into a long ride between two hedges. Suddenly she felt her legs start to go funny again, just like the time before on the hills. She had been sedated again but this time there were people following her. She just had to keep going whatever she felt like. She came to the end of the ride and glanced behind her. Yes, there were the men coming steadily along, not rushing or shouting, just coming along relentlessly.

Honey summoned up all her strength and jumped the five-barred gate at the end of the ride into a field of sheep. These sheep were just as used to her now as the sheep were on the hills and didn't take the slightest bit of notice as she slipped into the centre of the flock. A lot were lying down, dozing in the sun. Honey dropped onto her stomach and, crawling along with her head bent low, crept all through the flock. As her colour matched the sheep beautifully her camouflage was perfect. She reached the far end of the field and, silent as a ghost, disappeared into the hedge. With the biggest effort of will, she continued, travelling back round in a circle to reach the orchard where she would feel safe. She just about dragged herself into her nest under the pear tree and collapsed into a deep, drugged, sleep.

By next morning, the sedation had worn off and she woke up and wondered if it had all been a bad dream. Were there dreadful men following her? She stretched and crept out of her nest, sniffing the air carefully. No, there was no sign of life apart from the usual birds and cows. Honey went out into the cows' field. It was earlier than she had been getting up lately but she had gone to bed much earlier than was her wont these days, due to the drugged food she had eaten. She thought she might as well check her food spot to see if there was anything there but, of course, it was morning not evening so there was nothing there. She had a long drink and scented round. Yes, there was the scent of the men, she had not dreamt it after all. She retraced her steps and the steps of the men. She found the spot where they had hidden, waiting and watching for her to eat the drugged food. She retraced the steps over the first gate, along the ride and over the second gate. Then she found a spot where they had sat down and waited. Then they had travelled all round the field and simply returned the way they had come and left. Honey suddenly shivered, even though the weather was sunny and warm. What did it all mean? She had felt dreadful again and could not understand what was going on. Whatever would happen next?

There were no more interruptions to her life for quite some time. Day followed day except that the summer had drawn to its end and autumn was well-advanced. The nights were now getting longer and colder. It also rained a great deal more. Honey was glad of her warm dry nest these cold nights. She would lie all curled-up and cosy, listening to the rain outside steadily falling on the tree above her, knowing dinner would come every night and there were always some scraps to be found on the tip to supplement her food, if the magpies had too much of her dinner.

One day, she was as usual in her nest. It had been raining hard all night and Honey, who had never liked getting wet and disliked it even more as it grew colder, was sleeping in late. She was just thinking it might be an idea to go across to the tip for a quick scavenge for a late breakfast, as it had now stopped raining and was starting to dry up at last, when she heard a voice calling.

'Come out little dog.' It was a voice she knew, the voice

of the cowman. He was calling softly now, in the same gentle way that he had with the cows.

'I won't hurt you, little dog. Come on out,' he pleaded again. He wasn't quite by Honey's tree but was walking around the orchard hedge. He passed by, walking along the hedgerow and steadily walked round the whole orchard stopping every few steps to listen and look very carefully under the hedge. But Honey kept very still and quiet in her nest, waiting a long time before she came out, which she did very gingerly looking round her with great care and concentration, sniffing vigorously to scent if all was as it should be with no humans anywhere near about. All was quiet, the cowman had gone and was now several fields away. Honey slipped out of the orchard and trotted purposely off to the tip for her breakfast, somewhat delayed now, so the idea was all the more acceptable.

5

Life continued its uneventful way. Honey gained in confidence as she did not have any more scares to upset the equilibrium of her life. She did have a bit of a setback one day though but not too much to worry about. As she became more settled on the farm, she extended her boundaries and travelled further afield round the farm, sometimes onto neighbouring farms.She would inevitably see more farmers and farm workers but would slip away as soon as she either smelled or saw them. She had found a farm that had free range chickens and managed to find the occasional egg laid out which was a very welcome addition to her diet. One day, getting bolder by the day, she was trotting across the farmyard when she heard a man's voice shout, 'Where's my gun? Mary, there's that dog again.'

Honey flew and, luckily for her, the gun was not handy so she escaped once more. Honey did not go near that farmyard for a long time after that.

Winter was beginning to set in and October was drawing to its close. Honey was spending more time in her nest but was still enjoying the few fine days that came. Her coat was beginning to thicken up in preparation for the really bad weather to come. There had been several hard frosts earlier in the month and Honey had enjoyed the days of sun, still fairly warm on her back. Towards the end of the month there was quite a lot of rain. One Thursday was a very wet day indeed. Honey had stayed in her nest all day listening to the rain pouring down, dripping off the trees all around and above her. It had stopped, eventually, towards evening so Honey got up, stretched and popped out. She had her usual sniff of the air to make sure all was safe and well.

She was really hungry, as she had not been over to the tip for breakfast due to the wet weather, so she trotted confidently to see if her dinner was by the water trough as usual. But it wasn't. Nothing was there at all. There had only been a small meal the night before too. Honey sniffed about to see if there might be a few crumbs she might have missed but there was simply not a morsel about at all. Oh well, it would have to be the tip. Hopefully there would be a good meal there. On arrival, at the tip, she found a few bits but there did not seem to be very much there either so a somewhat disconsolate little dog crept back into her nest very much later in the night. It also started to rain again, even harder than the day before. It kept on until late into Friday evening.

Once again, Honey crept out of her nest and, with a very large hole in her tummy, a very hungry Honey went to the water trough for a drink and checked her food spot. Still no food. She just could not understand what could have happened. It had always arrived every day, without fail, for all of the four months she had been lost apart from the first ten days, but those days had been so dreadful she had tried to forget them, pushing them right back to the far recesses of her mind. They still came back to haunt her regularly in her dreams but, on waking, the days had been much better of late. Now suddenly things seemed to be going wrong again. Just when it was getting colder, and she needed food more, it had suddenly stopped. Honey spent the rest of the night hunting for anything she could think of or find.

She managed to catch an unwary mouse but it was such a small morsel it only filled a very small hole in a very hungry tummy. Even the tip seemed to be bereft of decent bits of food.

Honey, several times, checked her food spot to see if, by any magical touch, her food had suddenly reappeared but it was always the same, just plain empty. So, around four o'clock in the morning, a very tired and hungry puppy crept into her nest to try and sleep to forget her hunger. She catnapped for a few hours but woke up at her usual time, hunger gnawing at her. The weather had changed in the few hours she had slept and the morning was beautiful, much warmer than of late. the sun was shining down from a clear blue sky. Honey felt much better already. She would go and see the cows and check her food spot again, just to see if, by any luck, her dinner had reappeared.

She trotted along the orchard hedge and into the cows' field. Her nose twitched – surely she could smell food. It was too early for the cowman as yet but she trotted along to her dinner spot. Yes, there it was and very tempting indeed for such a hungry little dog. Honey did not stop to sniff or check for any unusual or different scents around her food. She just went straight for the dog meat with no thought in her head but breakfast at last. As she slipped through the barbed wire strands in the hedge she was suddenly brought up with a jerk. Something was tightly round her neck. She backed off in terror but she could not go backwards either and there was a dreadful tightening around her neck, cutting into her throat and choking her.

Then a man came out from the thickest part of the hedge, and ran towards her. Honey had been so intent on the smell of food she had not even stopped to check if all was well. She would have most likely not have scented him anyway as he had carefully stayed down wind of the food so she would not have any idea he was near. He talked softly to her, trying to soothe her terror at this sudden appearance, but he had to work fast. Honey was tightening the snare, as that was what she had slipped her head into. It would steadily tighten and throttle her. The man began to release the upper part of the snare where it had been tied above the food. Honey, who was by now in a state of blind panic through terror of the man being so close and the pain of the snare round her neck, bit at the nearest thing she could reach which turned out to be the mans wellingtons.

Then the snare released its grip and some of the pain went from Honey's neck, but before she could race off, she was firmly held and a sack was popped over her head to prevent her biting again. She was picked up bodily and carried, struggling hard, over a couple of fields. She heard a van door being opened. she was plonked in the back, the sack was removed from her head and the door slammed. There was a grill between the back of the van and the driver's seat. Honey sat dead still, the snare still hanging loosely round her neck. The man climbed into the driver's seat and, with a gusty sigh, turned on the engine and started to drive home.

Honey was sitting very quietly indeed. She had always quite liked the car and this was just the same except she didn't have any windows to look out of except the two small ones on the doors and they were too high up anyway. She was also still very scared indeed and had no idea of what was going to happen to her so if she sat very still and quiet things might get better with a bit of luck. The drive did not take long. They soon arrived at the man's house. The engine was turned off and the man climbed out and disappeared. Poor Honey sat in the back of the van and waited for what seemed like ages. Her neck was hurting where the snare had dug into the flesh and it was still hanging down her front. Although the time seemed to drag by for Honey it was really not very long. Honey suddenly heard the noise of another car engine drive up and park just by the side of the van she was sitting in. Car doors were opened and slammed shut, footsteps going away, a doorbell ringing, then voices. Was that a voice she used to know? Was it Suzanne's voice? Suddenly the van doors opened and she heard the man saying something about 'Be careful, she bit my wellington' but it was all lost as another voice, a much-loved voice, was saying 'Honey, where ever have you been?' and she was scooped up into loving arms and kissed and hugged and petted.

Honey went into ecstasies of delight and joy. She licked, wriggled and squirmed. This was what she had dreamed of for all the long months she had been lost, to be back with her real family again. She was held in Suzanne's arms for about ten minutes whilst they talked then she was popped into the back of her own car. At last safe and sound. She sat quiet and content for a few minutes whilst Suzanne went into the house but she was soon out and driving home talking to Honey all the time. It was only ten minutes down the road to home. Honey was carefully carried into the house and put down on the kitchen floor. Home at last. She was overjoyed. She rushed to first one dog bed and collected its blanket, then to the next, collecting its blanket, and finally popped all the blankets into the last bed, proudly holding the best blanket in her mouth. She put herself on top of the pile of blankets in the dog bed and sat there, head held high as if to say: 'There you are folks, I'm really home now!'